AMERICAN FEMALE

a true tale of adventure

Emily Carpenter

2016

EMILY CARPENTER

Some names and identifying details have been changed to protect the privacy of individuals. All events have been recounted to the author's best ability.

Written by Emily Carpenter

Edited by Anne Schweitzer & Darian Wigfall

Cover Design by Abigail Gallagher

Doo Doo Style Publication

Version 1   2016

Printed and bound in the United States of America.

ISBN: 0-9971422-0-4

ISBN-13: 978-0-9971422-0-4

For information about permission to reproduce selections from this book, write to amfembook@gmail.com

www.americanfemalebook.com

DEDICATION

To my parents:
Although you may try to deny it,
Everything I am –
Is only because of you.

CONTENTS

ACKNOWLEDGMENTS

First and foremost, thank you to my family, Robin and Kurt, Beth, Alex, Darin, and Bebe, who have always supported - in every way possible - all of my endeavors. I am forever grateful for my mentor, Richard Callow, who helped me see myself as a writer. To Miles Ross, for your gifts of inspiration to help me make it through the struggle. And Anne Schweitzer, who did the dirty work of editing early manuscripts and removing (most of) the f-and-c-bombs. Heartfelt thanks go to Carla Freiman Feuer, who schooled me on the publishing game, along with Darian Wigfall, who has also been an incredibly selfless resource and motivator.

So much gratitude to the adventurers around the world and my MCA Day peeps for keeping my dream-making capabilities alive. To all 300+ literary agents who rejected my manuscript, for forcing me to just do the damn thing myself. And everybody else along the way – you know who you are.

PART I
THE BEGINNING

1 STUCK-IN-AN-ELEVATOR SPEECH

The evening we arrived in Beijing, I hosted a get-together in Rune's hotel suite. The senator and distinguished businessmen assembled, gin and tonics with the perfect ratio of ice-to-Hendrick's were poured, and Rune's weird robot music played in the background. The group burst into laughter as I delivered the punchline to a joke about my hometown. Rune sat on a bar stool alone, looking surly.

"Emily," he barked. "I need more minutes for my Asia phone. You need to go get a top-up now."

It was 12:45 am. I looked over with a slight hint of disbelief in my eyes before quickly fixing them. I didn't need him going off the deep end in front of everyone.

"Okay," I affirmed. I turned to the guests, apologized, and excused myself.

With a face burning bright as a Christmas light, I retrieved my bag from the bedroom. Not only was I mortified; I was about to be extremely cold. Rune knew full well that I stupidly did not bring a coat with me. It had been the topic of discussion from the moment we stepped off the bullet train.

The temperature was significantly lower in Beijing than our previous city, but Rune denied me his extra coat for the duration of the trip.

"That will teach you a lesson you won't forget," he said.

Men in the group offered to retrieve the top-up for me while others expressed concern for my safety. Someone presented me with a warm wool coat. I wanted to take it but knew I couldn't. I smiled at them awkwardly as Rune looked on, waiting for me to misstep. I wouldn't give him the opportunity to flame me in front of them. I acted exactly as he wished.

"She's a big girl. She'll be fine," Rune said in a stern voice, ordering me along.

Swallowing my pride, I exited the suite, taking refuge in the hallway. I felt like an idiot.

What the fuck was my life?

I signed on to pay my dues and no one could say I hadn't done that. Putting up with his poor treatment because it was better than no opportunities, I didn't really have the luxury of a breakdown at the moment. There was a mission at hand to complete or there would be hell to pay. Who was I kidding, there would be hell to pay regardless, but returning with a top-up might lessen it a bit.

I braced myself for the cold and marched out into the quiet darkness, illuminated only by streetlight. The biting wind slapped my face and I began shivering. I'd only been in the city for an hour or two and knew nothing about Beijing. I felt like Rune sent me on a wild goose chase to punish me for something, maybe for people liking me. But I wouldn't be thwarted that easily.

One Year Earlier...

I received an invitation for supper with a man named Rune Andromeda during mid-December. Winter in St. Louis can feel like you're in the Arctic Circle. The weather is enough to make you hibernate until spring, which I normally did, unless I had an important business meeting with a future boss who had promised me a trip to Asia and beyond.

Rune owned a start-up camera bag business named Click!. I was recruited to fill a position called Deputy Director. The job description itself didn't exist, loosely described by Rune in vague emails as "training to take over the company," but I was told massages, unlimited vacation, and lattes were regular perks. Travel would be frequent and international, challenges inevitable.

Reservations abounded when I received the job offer. It didn't include traditional benefits. I had never considered a job without health insurance before. Additionally, a good portion of my pay would be based upon performance, the definition of which was not clearly outlined.

I was torn between comfort and the risky unknown, even though I knew I was bored with the status quo. My inherited family values were very Midwestern, living life by the principle of the matter, not leaning into the unfamiliar, always toward security and stability. Ingrained in me, they were never the perfect fit but had been comfortable enough. Now they were strangling me.

Alas, international travel was the ultimate hook at Click!. It was an experience I wanted and would do almost anything for. A bargaining chip during my recruitment process, it continued as a topic of discussion throughout my first dinner with Rune.

His restaurant choice was the most elite eatery in St. Louis at the time. This fell perfectly in line with my developing perception of him. I wasn't sure how to dress. Begrudgingly accepting the fact that my level of attractiveness was just as effective in business settings as intelligence and experience, I decided to use it to my advantage. Professional success was one of my top priorities, and this was the start of my wade into the gray ocean of business.

I ended up adorning my athletic, pale-skinned 5'8" frame in skinny black slacks, a scoop-neck black tank, beige shawl, and chocolate-brown heeled riding boots. My dishwater-blonde hair was pulled into a side-swept bun, and my large, cat-shaped eyes were glittering blue sapphires lined in charcoal. Over-sized lips slathered in Chapstick sat beneath my pierced nose, beside a Cindy Crawford beauty mark.

I arrived early, as I am wont to do. Taking a seat at the bar, thoughts of what our dinner would be like floated through my mind. Fiddling with my ring, vintage yellow gold and diamond 'E', I twisted it around my finger while glancing out the window.

There he was, dressed in dark gray slacks and a Merino wool sweater I would soon find out was his all-time favorite, with a beige scarf tied around his neck. He was much more petite than I remembered, standing several inches shorter than myself. His hair was blonde and squinty eyes bluish-green. He wasn't a very conventionally attractive man, but would prove to be such a unique individual that his appearance was often overlooked. However, his teeth were mangled, heaped together in a crooked pile front and center. They could be fixed, but he was the type of person who refused to conform, or just wanted people to think that he was too cool to care. We were very similar.

He entered the room with purpose and informed the hostess that he had arrived, only then speaking to me. We took our seats at the small table for two. A three-course meal was offered that evening. The only choice we had was how our steak would be prepared. I ordered mine well. Rune looked at me, aghast.

"You will not be eating a steak well done. They have the best cuts in the city." He then turned to the waitress, "Prepare her steak medium rare."

I was momentarily speechless at his gall. From that moment on, I had Rune pegged as intelligent, and suffering from Napoleon-syndrome.

Our conversation was Rune 101, with him rattling off facts about himself for over an hour. Born in Nebraska, he lived in a trailer park with no heat. His father was a drug addict, and his mom "checked out" when he was seven, whatever that meant. Rune wrote a book about how clocks worked and toured the states surrounding Nebraska promoting it when he was six years old. A decorated track runner, he broke his own record for fastest mile at his high school every year. His early twenties were spent backpacking throughout Europe, becoming a

French-trained sous chef.

His significant other of almost ten years was named Tilda. She was from Nebraska as well, but across the other side of the tracks. Her family was wealthy and connected to the oldest cheese factory in the United States. Before moving to St. Louis, they lived together in Texas and Oklahoma, where he was a professional cyclist. A vegan for seven years then vegetarian for three, he went full-on carnivore after crushing his pelvis in a cycling accident, unable to recover without protein.

Rune loved dogs and rescued two, but missed his stray cats he adopted in Nebraska when he was a homeless teen. His dogs were set to be the beneficiaries of his will. He didn't really care for America and planned to move out of the country if he could get Tilda to agree. There was a time when he bathed in a cold stream outdoors every day.

I could tell he liked talking about himself and his accomplishments, so I took the bait, asking more questions.

Rune was quadrilingual and a grade-five rock climber. Possessing only a high school education, he saw no value in institutional learning. In addition to Click!, he had started ten businesses, "including a fashion company," he emphasized in a transparent attempt to relate to me. Click! caused him to travel the majority of the year, mostly in Asia.

He was a Buddhist and photographer, who only drank hot green tea. IQ-wise, Rune was considered a genius. He used to build computers for a living, as well as performing home repairs. A fellow *Lord of the Rings* fan, he introduced me to the game of *Settlers of Catan*, which I would soon learn was boring as shit but somehow fun.

Near the end of our dinner, he looked at me and asked, "Are you okay traveling internationally with me?"

I was intrigued. He was an innovative individual, if not a bit odd and pretentious. I was positive I could put up with the nonsense in order to gain such valuable experience.

"Of course; I look forward to it," I responded confidently.

He smiled, a peculiar look on his face. "We'll see," he said.

That set the tone. My first day would be January 1, as Click! "doesn't celebrate holidays." An email account was activated in my name within the hour, receiving fifteen emails from Rune that evening. And so it began.

2 THE DEVIL WEARS MERINO WOOL

Rune instructed me to "dress smart" at the office. He wanted staff to respect me as if I were him. I didn't know what to expect, but the office was super casual. I had on a suit and our IT Director was wearing sweatpants.

I was to be Rune's right-hand man, as well as eyes and ears. For all intents and purposes, I *was* Rune. I was everyone's boss, the executive decision maker when he was not available, and the leader of morale. I was to consider the company as my own, spending as much money on anything I wanted, as long as I decided it was justified. It could be a thousand-dollar pizza party to 'maintain morale,' which was of utmost importance to Rune, although he could never spell it. Even in the accounting books it lists 'Moral.'

The staff at Click! had a basic setup with a standard curmudgeon IT guy, a token older white male in customer service, a quirky part-time bookkeeper, and a reserved graphic designer. Our tight-knit, bare-bones staff was filled out by a few all-stars.

Luca was Canadian and Asian, living and working remotely in the snowy mountains of Japan. Multi-talented, he was our bag designer when he wasn't snowboarding or taking kick-ass photos. Luca was nearing forty and decisive about whom he interacted with, as his cool wasn't for everyone. A hipster before hipsters existed, down to his disheveled black hair, over-sized glasses, flannel shirts, and devil-may-care attitude.

A first generation Vietnamese-American kid from Kansas, Remy always had a fresh fade, his fine black hair lined to precision, sharp as his piercing eyes. He could usually be found in the office drooling over a car show or watching tutorials on the newest gadgets from behind his thin spectacles. Gentle, silly, and non-confrontational, he handled Click!'s team of big-name photographers, which we utilized as ambassadors the same way tennis shoe companies integrate basketball players into their marketing efforts. Most of the top adventure photographers in the world used Click! camera bags and Remy was their connection for free stuff.

These photographers were rugged, do-whatever-it-takes-to-get-the-shot kind of guys. The type to hike twenty miles into the jungles of Africa, hang off the side of a helicopter above a mountain in the Himalayas, scaffold the side of an ice-covered glacier in Antarctica. They traveled to the remote, unknown, third-world corners of the planet and back, dirt bag camping in deserts unbathed for days, risking their lives, literally and figuratively, to fulfill their passions and capture the perfect vista.

I gobbled up their unique stories of personal dedication to doing what they loved. Bucking convention, the guys surged forward pioneering their crafts, undaunted by a lack of path to follow, simply creating their own. Their creativity and courage was violently contagious. I found myself wishing that I had been brave enough to take a risk to do what I loved when I was younger. I was only twenty-seven then, but in Midwestern years that was damn-near old-maid, spinster status.

Rune and I had a meeting during one of my first days at Click!. For ninety minutes straight, he rapid-fired a verbal rundown of all of his important business contacts, including the number of kids they had, how Rune met them, their favorite drinks, and preferred masseuse at their regular spa in Hong Kong. I was expected to remember all of this.

Rune spoke with careful intent, "You and I, primarily

you—and absolutely nobody else—will communicate with and handle important business relationships."

"Okay," I said, nodding my head in agreement.

"Any communication, calls, emails, texts, smoke signals, courier pigeons—anything—received from anyone you or I deem important, must go to you immediately. If Remy or whoever answers the phone and because of some wormhole glitch in our multidimensional galaxy, happens to talk to one of the factory owners and sounds like an idiot, that could royally fuck up everything we have going on here. The Chinese are very much about image. It's called 'face,' 'saving face.' You'll learn more about that before we leave for China."

My ears perked up. "And when is that?" I asked earnestly.

"Soon, young grasshopper, soon." He smiled and patted me on the head.

Rune had office rules. Listening to music was acceptable, but lyrics were not. Eating at desks was strictly prohibited. Participating in the staff lunch in the kitchen was strongly encouraged, considered a tool for building camaraderie and devotion to the company.

Everyone was required to take a twenty-minute walk each workday, Rune's long game to incrementally better the staff's health, resulting in increased productivity. All of his decisions were Trojan horses. A myriad of unwritten rules existed, one of which dictating that whenever Rune felt like strolling down to the pub for a cider, we were obliged to join him. His staff was his built-in social circle.

Vacation time was unlimited but the relentless pressure to work, work, work kept the Click! staff apprehensive to take any time off at all. Performance pay was awarded quarterly and based on Rune's personal feelings toward the person in question on that particular day. Often, he would use one error committed months prior to deprive staff of thousands of dollars.

Joining Click!'s wellness plan was described as optional, yet Rune's constant bullying of staff drinking soda or eating fast food was unbearable. I quickly shaped up my eating habits, not wanting to fall in Rune's line of fire. He was a health freak and didn't trust Western medicine. Instead, he subscribed to Chinese medicine, massage, acupuncture, chiropractic, and meditation.

Rune pressured me to be treated immediately upon learning that I suffered from migraines. I was prescribed a strict regimen of chiropractic care, energy healing, and massage, completed by a gym membership with a lap swimming pool, and gadgets to track every heartbeat, step, and calorie. While it may seem like care and concern, Rune was simply grooming me to be in tip-top workhorse shape. He operated on the theory that by removing daily hardships, his employees would be more focused and productive. It was true. Maslow would have been proud.

My loyalty was cultivated strategically, starting with a brand-new Samsung Galaxy Note I happily accepted. What I didn't realize in the moment was that I was trading my life right then and there. Rune expected complete access to me. He wasn't shy about it either—emailing, texting, or even calling at 3:30 am.

To maximize our time together while he was in town, I adopted Rune's erratic global office hours. Working any given hour of the day and sleeping for a spell when I became exhausted, it all blurred together. Click! soon dominated every waking moment of my life, eight days a week.

We ate at least two meals together every day, with him cooking or buying, but providing my food nonetheless. Breakfast, either a slinger from his favorite café down the street, scrambled eggs and oatmeal handmade in the kitchen from organic ingredients, or a red-eye frozen pizza, would take place anywhere from 3:00 am – 8:00 am, and lunch always around noon. Hot green tea was a constant. Yet to acquire a taste for tea at lunch, I was relegated to water, due to the unwritten 'no soda' rule.

Rune treated me like his new best friend, confiding intimate details of his life and showering me with extra attention. Every few days, I would find a gift on my desk. Plump, upmarket dark chocolates dusted with salt crystals, heavenly scented lotions in travel-sized bottles, a link to a cool Beastie Boys mix, homemade lattes, and tickets to theater shows; it was never ending. Banning traditional Chapstick by throwing away my cherry tube one day, a stick of natural Pomegranate Oil Burt's Beeswax appeared the next morning.

Rune sent my boyfriend, Saleem, and I to some of the top restaurants and events in St. Louis.

"Because you fucking work your ass off," he said.

No truer words had ever been spoken. I appreciated the gestures.

Saleem stood 6'7". Rune insisted on having a California King bed delivered to our house. He paid special attention to Saleem, referring to the two of them as peas in a pod. Rune considered Saleem and myself a less extreme version of he and Tilda, a 5'7" ghostly-white waif with teacup features, wispy brown hair, and an uppity attitude.

Rune and Saleem both came from poor families, surviving on welfare growing up. Tilda and I were intelligent women with strong convictions. The main difference between the men being that Rune was driven to achieve while Saleem was a laid-back hippie who sought low-hanging fruit. The main differences between Tilda and I were the facts that I didn't come from money or attend a prestigious school, and I wasn't a stuck-up, condescending bitch.

They didn't have many friends, so Rune was always forcing us on dinner dates and canoe trips. Our time spent together was always awkward, as Tilda was not very personable and Rune was, well, Rune. The four of us squished into a cab one night for an uncomfortable ride to compulsory cocktails. Passing a restaurant Saleem insisted we try a few nights prior, I attempted to make small talk with Tilda.

"Saleem and I went to that restaurant the other night. It wasn't my favorite but Saleem really liked it. Have you ever been there?" I pointed to it.

Glancing out the window, Tilda scoffed, turning her nose

up in the air. In all seriousness, she looked at me and said, "What makes you think Rune and I would ever eat at a pedestrian restaurant?"

What a cunt. I made every effort to avoid Tilda after that night.

Rune was extreme. At times impatient, his words were short and snappy, with zero tolerance for error. He justified his hasty actions by citing his "well-known, incredibly high standards." Militantly anti-religion when it conflicted with his beliefs, he would bite my head off if I said "bless you" to his sneezes.

In rare instances, he seemed to project care and concern. Sporadically, I would be mandated to chill out and play hooky. When I found out mid-work day that my favorite musician, Adam Yauch, AKA MCA from the Beastie Boys, passed away, Rune sent me home to grieve. His mood fluctuated at a rapid pace. It was exhausting.

Over the course of our relationship, Click!, Rune, and I became one: co-managing every aspect of his being, business and personal. I was given full access to Rune's email, free to search, read, and respond as him as needed. I possessed a master list of Rune's passwords, usernames, pin numbers, security questions and answers, and multiple sets of instructions in case of his incarceration, extortion, ransom, or death.

Rune's globetrotting lifestyle was in my hands, booking his flights, hotels, trains, cars, dinner reservations, meetings, and more. I was the gatekeeper renewing and applying for rushed passports and visas at the last-minute. I doubt I'll ever forget his social security number.

I scheduled Rune's favorite stylist and masseuse for in-house haircuts and massages before he headed out on his month-long business trips across the Atlantic Ocean. Handling his matters while he was gone, I made sure his out-of-state plates were renewed, favorite shoes repaired by a reputable cobbler, and sourced a Buddhist temple for him to visit when he returned.

Working under his aegis, my duties encompassed all things Rune deemed necessary for Click! to function, ranging from preparing reports for the Board of Directors to performing marketing research, developing policies and procedures, writing proposals for funding, coordinating staff activities, managing the office, recruiting, hiring, disciplining and firing employees, putting out daily customer service fires, crafting a global communications strategy, and on and on. Anything you can imagine, I did it.

His delivery was curt, snobby, and straight up rude at times; somehow I managed to sort out the shit from the gold, discard the former, and learn from the latter. The life lessons gleaned from the first few months alongside Rune I could never sufficiently explain. He taught me the most efficient way to search for the best flights, the meaning of a media kit, and how to create a relationship from a cold email.

I picked up his love of *Harvard Business Review*, ambient electronica, and tendency to pop up out of deep sleep and open my laptop at 3:00 am with the desire to work. His asinine belief that he could do anything was fresh, infectious, and mirrored my own. When we first met, I told him I could do anything. Now he had me balls deep in everything.

Although I spent most of my time absorbed in intimate, minute details of Rune's life, it often felt like *I* was his main project. Rune drilled it into my brain every single day to "stop being afraid of failure." He made it his mission to "un-teach what school taught me." We were the same in many ways, driven to do, be, and achieve, often at the expense of our personal relationships and work-life balance. However, Rune was capable of maintaining a cool, calm, collected demeanor through the stress and uncertainty. I had a different way of going about it.

I viewed the Deputy Director position with Click! as my golden egg. All I ever wanted was the chance to work hard and prove my value. My proximity to Rune, new responsibilities, and future global experiences were exactly the opportunity I sought. I wouldn't fuck it up. My ironclad, uber-professional armor protected me at all times.

Severe yet reserved, every word that came out of my mouth was carefully considered. Constantly scrambling under the eye of Rune, I was obsessed with having it all together, at all times. There was no one to lean on. Even if I had support, I wouldn't have asked for help. Never saying no, I balanced on the swaying tightrope alone, refusing to disappoint Rune.

Every single thing I touched had to be strategically executed. If not, Rune would rake me over the coals, nitpicking my deficiencies to death. It was difficult to keep track of our millions of objectives and plans of attack. He always had a Machiavellian angle that sometimes I didn't recognize or understand. Breaking it down to me in painfully condescending, explain-like-I'm-five language, he built my sociopathic skills one manipulative lesson at a time.

A hypersensitive, perfectionist people-pleaser, I incessantly rewrote reports, searched for cheaper flights, and obsessed over insignificant details, worrying for hours about every single thing that could go wrong. I was hesitant and unsure. None of my previous positions had prepared me for the duties of this job.

I had no idea what the fuck I was doing most of the time. Trusted with an immense amount of responsibility, this also provided me an opportunity to seriously screw up the company. Never failing to defer to Rune when he was around, I always wanted to make the decision that he would have made, and do everything right the first time. Perfection wasn't the goal. It was all I would accept.

Rune had an odd way of encouraging. Leading by example, his motivation and extreme determination seeped into my life immediately. Although our interactions didn't leave me feeling warm and fuzzy, Rune awkwardly yet effectively encouraged *doing*, through trial and error, mistakes and failure. Exasperated with my fear-based mindset, he forcefully reminded me that nothing was impossible; no dream was too big. His voice was always cold but bore confounding wisdom.

"You're too rigid, Emily. Your mind operates within a box; you have no creativity. You and you alone are the only thing holding you back. Right now you're incapable of making your own decisions and trusting yourself. You aren't really living. You're uncultured, earth-bound, unenlightened. You're so worried about everything. If you want to make your problems seem small, find bigger problems."

He repeated this mantra to me day in and day out, a skipping vinyl on a record player.

"I will break you," he said, his eyes gleaming in anticipation of a challenge.

I smiled meekly, not fully understanding what he meant. I would soon learn, whether I wanted to or not. Rune set out to force enlightenment upon me. It didn't matter to him the means, as long as he reached his desired outcome in the end. This was his outlook on life.

I had been working at Click! for two months when Rune informed me that he had found my counterpart during a trip to China. His name was William Sandstone. There were numerous Williams and Bills within Rune's circles so we decided he would be known as Sandstone and focus on our logistics and mathematical stuff, while I handled the rest.

Sandstone had been working in Zhuhai, China for the past year with our industry friend, Large Larry from Lansing (a self-imposed nickname), at his manufacturing company, Dumbo. Two days after receiving Large Larry from Lansing's blessing, Sandstone was buckling up for a seventeen-hour flight headed for good old St. Louis, Missouri, USA. He was talked up by Rune, who described him as a "super sharp kid with a degree in Economics, some international experience, and a fuckload of potential." I would decide for myself.

I received a long-winded email from Sandstone the night before he arrived. It was a friendly note to say hello, describe himself a bit, and confess his age, which was twenty-two. He later informed me that he was a bit nervous and downed a few gin and tonics before pressing send. Sandstone's temporary home would be the guest bedroom of our office.

My response was half-genuine. On one hand, I was overloaded and overworked. I could definitely use another pair of exceptional eyes and hands to divide my workload and help move projects forward. On the other hand, I was slightly jealous, not wanting to give up my spot of Rune's favorite and smartest in the room. I shillyshallied between anticipation and dubious curiosity before Sandstone's arrival.

However, from the first moment we met, I was 100% glad Sandstone was there. No matter how smart I was, I couldn't do everything alone. Standing 5'10" with bushy eyebrows, dark brown hair cut short on the sides, green eyes, and a defined chin, he was usually clad in his favorite navy blue cardigan, slacks, and dress shoes. Unless it was the weekend, when we both wore flip-flops and T-shirts.

He had only met Rune for a few hours before accepting the job offer and there was no way he could have any idea what he was getting himself into. Only twenty minutes of his employment with Click! had passed when Rune ruthlessly scolded Sandstone about the formatting of a trivial email written to a nobody, about nothing important. I considered him jumped in.

We shared a sarcastic, dry, and twisted sense of humor, love of *Lord of the Rings*, and obsession for knowledge and achievement. Although Sandstone could be a total douche at times, I often gave him a pass, chalking it up to the fact that he was a twenty-two year old dude chiefly interested in *Settlers of Catan* and online gaming. Forming a brother and sister bond from the get-go, it was clear to me that Sandstone and I had starkly different backgrounds.

Sandstone hailed from an upper middle class family in a bright white neighborhood, schooled in private institutions then transported out of state to experience a top-tier education and expand his mind in sunny California. His vocabulary, composed of fancy talk, told tales of early morning hikes through the forest, smoking Cali Kush, and listening to Velvet Underground on vinyl.

Sandstone graduated from college and went to live it up and work in China. He knew nothing about the middle class Midwest. We were perfect counterparts, providing each other new perspectives, realities, and possibilities.

Sandstone couldn't stand my lack of culture. He hated my eating habits, voicing his disgust for traditional American palettes, angrily urging me to try spicy salsas, curries, and mystery dishes. I scoffed at Sandstone's privileged lifestyle and rigid beliefs. I didn't grow up hurting, but I knew a lot of people who did.

We pushed each other past our comfort zones each day. Debating and arguing at times, Sandstone knew I was capable and didn't give me the option to slack off or make excuses. His unwavering persona didn't often need my encouragement or confidence boosting, but I gave it freely anyway. I respected his aspirations and willingness to take risks. We both knew more about the world through our interactions with each other.

Rune always made a big deal about how he never took holiday, and decided to accompany Tilda to Bhutan, India. Crowned the happiest place on Earth, Bhutan is exclusive. Prospective visitors must apply and be approved for a visa to enter, and once within the country, all tourists are required to be accompanied by guides. While Rune was in Bhutan, Sandstone and I were both a little freaked out with the amount of responsibility he left us with. We were expected to manage the office and take on Rune's duties, including maintaining a very important business relationship dependent upon the prompt arrival of a shipment of Click! goods, in addition to our overwhelmingly long daily to-do lists, topping seventy-five-plus 'critical' tasks each.

Sandstone and I decided it would be in our best interest to pull Friday all-nighters, breaking for dinner then returning to the office. It was insane, but it worked for us. Rocking out to a mix of Eminem, CCR, Marvin Gaye, Devendra Banhart, and Black Sabbath, Elvis-inspired dance parties would break out when we could no longer bear to look at the computer screens in front of us. We drank at our desks, me sipping a bottle of hard apple cider, Sandstone with aged scotch on the rocks. He was such a snob.

Sandstone was responsible for ensuring timely delivery of our important shipment from China. The third day of Rune's holiday in Bhutan, Sandstone had a decision to make between ground and air shipment, resulting in either a significantly later date of delivery, or on-time delivery with a significant cost increase, to the tune of $20,000. Rune had just gone offline for eighteen hours. A response was required within a window of six; Rune didn't reply to emails or answer his phone.

Sandstone and I racked our minds for hours, listing pros and cons, attempting to analyze the situation from each stakeholder's perspective. Ultimately the decision was Sandstone's, and it had to be made within the next fifteen minutes or the option for air shipment would expire. We were stressed, gulping black coffee, pacing back and forth pulling out our hair like madmen. I stepped outside for smoke breaks every few minutes.

Down to the last two hundred and forty seconds, Sandstone made the executive decision to ship the goods by air, incurring the $20,000 fee but meeting the deadline. I supported him. We left the office for the day well after 7:00 pm at night.

My cell phone rang at 4:00 am. It was Rune, calling from Bhutan.

Fuck. This can't be good, I thought to myself.

I was right. The air shipment turned out to be the absolute wrong decision. He was angry. I was to ensure Sandstone fixed the error immediately, recovering all $20,000. Rune sent Sandstone to the office thirty minutes prior to my wake up call.

"He doesn't get to sleep until this is fixed," he snarled, hanging up on me.

No matter how hard he tried, Sandstone was only able to reduce the cost of the air shipment by a few thousand dollars, and this wasn't accomplished until months later. Although Rune encouraged mistakes through decisive action, and left

Sandstone with the power to make a $20,000 error, he still withheld performance pay from Sandstone for an entire year, citing the shipping incident.

We became a wolf pack of two, defending each other from Rune daily, picking up the pieces after he verbally destroyed us for something preposterously inconsequential. When Rune was on a rampage it was more than recommended to stay out of his way. He went off on tangents, lashing out nonsensically. This was mostly directed toward Sandstone since he was the lowest on the totem pole among the three of us.

Rune always touted me as superior, rubbing it in Sandstone's face. Thankfully, Sandstone never became resentful toward me. It just brought us closer together because we both knew it could change at any minute. I couldn't stand it when he would pick Sandstone apart.

"You're not very smart, are you, Sandstone? You should be more like Emily."

"Gaining some weight there, fat boy. You're a mess, Sandstone, look at you."

"You can't get any girls, Sandstone. I bought you an extra-large bottle of lotion."

No one dared to respond.

Rune liked to say that his team would run into a wall for him. It was true. We were foot soldiers wearing blinders, trusting and never questioning our commander. When he said jump, we marched to the tallest building and leapt without delay. In Click!'s kingdom, Rune was the smartest, the best, all-knowing, alpha male. One Rune to rule them all.

3 TING BU DONG

I was ecstatic to be confined to a plane for 8,000+ miles. A crisp, navy blue passport had been issued to me but the pages remained blank, save for the wanderlust inspiring quotes from great Americans embossed throughout—which I had read countless times. I was finally venturing beyond the borders of the United States and would be gone for almost an entire month.

Passing through Hong Kong, Zhuhai was the first stop, located in the Guangdong Province with a population of 1.4 million, considered a small city in China. Living at the Click! apartment, I would work with our new Asia-based partner company, Dumbo, helping them get up to speed. They would be our boots-on-the-ground in China, and supply chain eyes and ears at the factories where our bags were produced. Next I would facilitate a company meeting in Macau, the Vegas of the World, hitting Zhuhai and Hong Kong again before returning home.

I didn't worry about leaving Saleem behind for so long. He wasn't going anywhere. He was content, and I wore the pants anyway.

July in Zhuhai would no doubt be searing and sticky. Our shared office space at Dumbo was casual. Dresses and summery clothes were my chosen wardrobe. I didn't pack nearly as much clothing as someone normally would because my suitcase was already full. Rune had shamelessly pressured me into smuggling a hefty amount of Click! product across the Chinese border in my personal luggage.

"I do it all the time. It's a gray area. You worry too much," he said, condescendingly.

I complied against my better judgment. After stowing away my bootleg goods, only about a fourth of my large purple suitcase space remained. I rolled up my clothing as tight as I could.

Rune and I were flying to Asia together since it was my first international flight. Remy was already in Zhuhai working on his design skills with the Dumbo crew and would meet us at the Hong Kong – China border upon our arrival.

We had a layover in Detroit before the long flight to Hong Kong so Rune led me to the special Delta Airline lounge, taking advantage of his Diamond Medallion status perks. Nothing too impressive—just chairs, cookies and drinks. It was clear Rune was very proud of his level of access.

"They serve my favorite biscuits in the Delta lounge. Very high quality. They're the only kind I'll eat. I enjoyed them on a private island with the Prince of Cashmere once," he said, insisting on being pretentious at all times. My natural response was one of contempt, but I forced a smile that I hoped looked genuine.

Making our way to our assigned row on the plane, Rune sacrificed his window view for me and took up residence in the middle seat. To his left was a handicapped man, utilizing crutch-like apparatuses to walk. The older gentleman, nearing his sixties, was less than twenty-four hours away from laying eyes on his true love for the first time.

They met through a religious dating service and after two years of talking on the phone, he was making the trek to China to see her in person and ask for her hand in marriage. A long, drawn-out conversation regarding challenges associated with visas for married partners from different countries ensued, with Rune proclaiming that he could get the deal done for this man, with no trouble at all.

Turning to me, he said, "Get his info and take care of it."

Rune loved to use me to fulfill the wildest dreams of complete strangers. These were often near-impossible feats, obtaining in just a few days American visas for Chinese citizens, or fraudulently titling two old school buses as RVs through Rune's dad's backstreet connections. I always came through, fighting my way out of the gauntlet Rune shoved me into.

Rune considered me his personal guanxi-generating slave. Explained best in three parts, guanxi involves the depth of feeling within an interpersonal relationship, the moral obligation to maintain the relationship, and the idea of 'face', meaning the combination of social status, propriety, and prestige. Guanxi exhibits qualities found more often in American friendships than American business relationships. At a certain point in the development of a relationship, guanxi provides comfort that individuals will consider each other's wants, needs, and best interests when making decisions, always saving face on both sides.

I learned during my first fifteen-hour flight that I am unable to sleep on planes. I tried using the tiny little cotton ball airlines call a pillow, with Rune relinquishing his in an attempt to double the fluffiness. Leaning against the wall, lying straight back, resting my head on my hands hunching over the tray— none of it worked for me. I would be awake for the duration of the flight.

Rune and I watched his favorite TV shows to pass the time. He supplied a splitter for the headphone output so we could both listen and offered me his blanket, but I figured I would let him keep that since I already had his pillow.

Rune often asked if I was excited.

I responded "of course," but never let my feelings show.

I was excited, but at the same time, I didn't really know how I felt or what to expect. Also, I was traveling with Rune. Despite all the amenities he provided, I couldn't relax around him. Rune just wasn't the type of person to let you get comfortable.

Always eager to exhibit his omnipotent knowledge, Rune hit me with a last-minute briefing on cultural competency in China.

"I know you're from St. Louis so this is especially important for you. When you hear 'nei ga', they aren't saying what you think they are. 'Nei ga' means 'that' in Mandarin."

"Oh. Good to know," I said sincerely.

"Also, tipping is not ingrained in their culture at this point and I don't want to disrupt the fragile socioeconomic climate, so no tipping." He looked me straight in the eye. "No assuming and no saying sorry. Ever."

I was guilty of over-apologizing, a rampant curse of womanhood. Rune put an end to that right away. My gaze never wavered and I didn't apologize for apologizing. Score.

He continued. "Remember to *always* accept business cards with both hands, avoid the number four, use the color red, and I hope you didn't buy any clocks as gifts."

I didn't. In Chinese culture, the number four, as well as clocks, were associated with death. I knew better. Our tokens to cultivate guanxi were all on-point. None predominantly white or black in color, and all accompanied by culturally relevant themed cards tucked in red envelopes.

Daydreaming about what the next few weeks of my life would be like, I couldn't wait to experience the aspects of China that had been so vividly described to me: steamed dumplings, endless massages, culture shock, blue-eyed blonde-hair minority status, suicide go-karts, tea ceremonies—all the excitement I had been fed by Rune and Sandstone. They thought I would be too nervous and scared to try anything new. They were wrong.

Almost a full day into our travels we began to descend into the misty wonderland of Hong Kong. I stared intently out the window. Smoggy clouds of pea soup submerged the mountains, leaving only their peaks visible as we flew over the water and onto the runway. Exiting the plane at the Hong Kong airport, we were thrown into a sea of black hair and light-complexioned skin. Everyone was moving at a hurried pace and there were *a lot* of people.

"Over here, grasshopper," Rune called to me from ten yards ahead. I snapped back to attention and caught up with him, my eyes round as an owl. I was in sensory overload, attempting to observe and commit to memory every single detail. Rune cackled, very much enjoying being present for my first experience on another continent.

"It's just the Hong Kong airport, kiddo. There are a lot more interesting things to see."

Weaving in and out of the crowd, we power-walked at a manic pace. Yelling over his shoulder as he marched down the left side of the people-mover, Rune drilled me about the customs and immigration process in a stern voice.

"Take out your passport." Shoving a piece of paper into my hand, he barked at me. "Complete this form. Stand in that line. Fucking smile. Don't look suspicious. Tell them you're here for business. If they ask more questions, say fashion. Declare nothing. Look like you belong here. *Act* like you belong here. If they ask what's in your suitcase, say they're your personal items you're bringing as gifts for your friends. You're a pretty white girl in Asia; you can do whatever you want. Flirt with them."

I was a little overwhelmed.

We took our places in the immigration line and began scribbling on the tiny square sheets of duplicate paper. One for entering China, one for exiting China.

"They should have given these to us on the plane so we would have them ready. They *normally* do," he said, sighing. I completed my form by balancing on one foot as I rested my passport on my knee while copying the passport number. Rune, of course, pointed out the fact that he used his passport so much he had his number memorized, and he added memorizing my passport number to my ever-growing to-do list.

I wasn't fully prepared for the scrutiny of a white girl crossing into Asia, or the suspense of smuggling goods into the country. Rune had gone over all of this with me in detail beforehand, but I guess I just had to experience it for myself. Doing something new for the first time can be awkward. Doing it with the potential of detainment in China is stressful, to say the least.

When I voiced my last-minute concerns, Rune shooed away my worries, saying that nobody would ever notice.

"If you're detained—which you won't be—you'll just receive a fine. I'll take care of it. Stop worrying," he snapped. Rune always proclaimed to be capable of handling any situation.

I neared the front of the line. Rune would follow behind me, to make sure I made it through. Immigration is a very strict place. A small light turned from red to green. The young Asian woman standing in line ahead of me approached the immigration booth.

Stepping up to the faded yellow line painted on the floor, it would be my turn next. My heart rate began to accelerate. Large thumps formed in my chest and I felt my internal temperature rise. I pleaded with my body not to flush bright red as it normally did when I got nervous.

When the light turned green, I cleared my throat and moved toward the booth, projecting the illusion of confidence. The immigration officer was a man, thank God. Relieved, I smiled and slid my passport across the faded gray counter. As I released it, the passport remained open to my China visa page. There was a faint sweat thumbprint from where I had been clenching it in my fist.

He looked at me and said "Nǐ hǎo," which means hello in Mandarin. I responded the same.

He grabbed my passport from the counter and studied it. I stood at the dirty terminal, tired and hungry from seventeen hours on planes, stimulated by my new surroundings, and on-edge about the acceptance of my visa and clearance into China. Once I passed through immigration, I would reach customs. I was scared about the possibility of customs opening my large purple suitcase to reveal carefully-stashed contraband. I tried to play it cool.

"Where are you from?" he asked in excellent English.

"St. Louis, Missouri," I said smiling and looking him in the eyes.

"What is your business here?" His voice was stern.

I momentarily panicked and looked away to the left, a rookie mistake when lying. Quickly returning my gaze to his, I remembered what Rune told me and blurted out the first thing that came to my mind.

"Fashion."

He continued to study my passport and suddenly deemed it worthy, ordering me to look into the camera. A small lens was positioned right above my forehead. A viewing screen next to it displayed my image. Centering my face, I smiled for the picture.

"Do not smile," he said in a disapproving tone.

Immediately I slacked my jaw, straightened up and stared somberly into the camera.

Stamp, stamp. He pounded his metal immigration stamp onto the pages of my passport and handed it back to me.

"Is that all?" I asked, waiting for permission to continue my journey past immigration. He had already switched the button to green and was beginning his interrogation of the next individual.

Rune and I collected our luggage from baggage claim and kept moving forward to the customs queue. I once again received the literal green light to approach the desk. This was the moment I had been dreading. I handed the officer my customs form, which indicated that I had nothing to declare. However, I did have something to declare, more like many things.

My heart raced as the time passed sluggishly. Every second was an hour, stuffed with possibilities of what the customs agent was thinking.

Was he looking at me strangely? Could he tell I was on the verge of freaking out? Was he noticing the deep red flush creeping up my neck? Did he care enough to ask me to open my suitcase? Does the fact that I'm a white female really give me any clout here? What would happen if I were caught? Would I be placed on a no-fly list? Would I be kept in Asia indefinitely? Could Rune even buy my way out?

The thoughts and worries churned around a whirlpool in my brain, settling in my gut. I felt like I was going to puke and nervously ran my un-manicured fingers through my hair, tucking it behind my ear.

"Nothing to declare?" the customs agent asked, peering out from behind his wire-rimmed glasses.

"No, sir," I responded automatically. I never say sir.

He ushered me through without a second glance. I breathed a sigh of relief, proud of myself for keeping cool. Rune was waiting for me near the exit.

"Good job, kiddo," he said, smiling.

Felix was flying from the Netherlands and joining us in China to do some photography work for Dumbo and act as a rep for our sponsored photography team at the company meeting in Macau. We were to pick him up at the Hong Kong ferry and journey together to the China border. He didn't have a working Asia phone, so we were banking on the fact that a mid-twenties, six-foot-something, blonde-haired, blue-eyed Dutch man would stand out among the crowd. We were right.

Felix could be best described as ski bum, pro photographer, soon-to-be doctor, dolphin trainer, and part-time male model. That pretty much sums it up.

Felix was unquestionably gorgeous, with strong Dutch features and thick unkempt locks. Kind and creative, he had the fit body of a skier, wild and insane personality, improbable smarts, and a super sexy Dutch accent where his th's sounded more like d's. He would be along for the ride at our apartment for the next few weeks.

After a less-than-smooth ferry voyage, we hopped in a taxi and arrived at the Hong Kong-China border. The driver removed the bungee cord securing our mountain of luggage hanging off the back of the cab as Rune counted out a few multi-colored notes known as Hong Kong Dollars; no tip. The three of us ran up the plaza to the long lines inside.

We didn't have much time. The border would close in less than an hour. Remy and Large Larry from Lansing awaited our arrival on the China side as we inched through the queue. Even though it was near midnight on a weekday, the lines were filled with hundreds of bodies, ants making their way through the farm tunnels.

"There's so many young people out," I commented.

"They all go to Hong Kong to do their shopping," Rune said, matter-of-factly.

I could tell. Everyone was dressed uniquely, rocking their own styles. All of the females wore heels. It didn't matter what type of shoe: pump, sandal, wedge, flip-flop, sneaker - they were all heeled. The girls were still shorter than me standing flat-footed. At the end of my trip I would determine that the heeled shoes had less to do with the height and more to do with the male-dominated and submissive female culture in Asia.

The three of us made it across the border to China.

"The White Devil has returned!" Large Larry from Lansing called out, waving to us as we approached the parking lot. The White Devil was Rune's nickname in China. He was known for getting Dumbo staffers wicked drunk and encouraging ill-advised behavior.

Larry looked just as you probably imagine: large, white, and round, with a putty face. Sandy russet hair, a fair amount for his age of mid-forties, fell into his shifty blue eyes that lit up when his thin lips arched into a smile, which was often. His daily uniform was either basketball shorts or khakis with a T-shirt and tennis shoes. Rune insisted we gift Larry fifteen pairs of sneakers on our trip over.

The five of us and our luggage would have to squish to fit into Larry's small four-door sedan. Rune hopped in the front seat.

"Remy, you're a fucking cupcake. Sit bitch," Rune said. "Make sure Emily has enough room." He smiled at me.

Felix and I squeezed in on either side of him. There were

no seat belts. I stared out the window the entire drive to the apartment. Everything was new; everything was interesting. I was in my element, curious and exploratory.

Rune nudged me out of my catatonic state. "See those really tall buildings over there?" he said, pointing across the bridge ahead of us.

I peered out into the darkness. We were approaching a complex of skyscrapers with small squares of lights illuminating the night through hundreds of identical windows and balconies. They looked just as Sandstone had described and the photos I Googled months before.

I nodded, entranced, "Yeah."

"That's our apartment, kiddo."

We made it safely off the roads of Zhuhai and continued into an underground parking garage that was filled to the brim with Aston-Martins, Mercedes, Maseratis, and Bentleys. The rubber of the tires squealed loudly as Larry looped around the parking lane to the elevator entrance. We dumped our collective luggage from the trunk into a pile on the parking garage floor. It was steamy and my hair immediately frizzed, shrinking into curls.

Sorting through the luggage, we hauled it into the tiny elevator lobby. There was no air conditioning and when the glass doors to the parking garage closed, the thick air was suffocating. LED lights above the elevators indicated it was making its way down from the seventy-seventh floor to our location on sub-floor one.

We were fast-melting ice cream cones, constantly wiping droplets from our temples and faces. All efforts were futile; we were mixing sweat with sweat and wiping it all over in a new place. Anything that wasn't moist before we touched it was drenched in human secretion after brief contact.

Our elevator finally arrived and half of us piled in. The other half waited behind for the next one. Elevator regulations in China are not as strict as they are in America and it is not unheard of for the elevators to get stuck, trapping passengers in a small contained space with no air, sometimes to the point of death.

We rode the steel death cage up to the fifty-seventh floor. Large Larry from Lansing, his Labradoodle, Biraffe, and his girlfriend, CC, lived on the forty-third floor, but were in full hosting mode, escorting us to our apartment, and practically holding our hands. Exiting the elevator into a narrow hallway, Larry led me to the last door on the left, my home for the next few weeks.

The apartment was a nice but simple four-bedroom, three-bathroom abode. Rune told me many times that our monthly rent was more than an average Chinese person made in an entire year. We were not living the normal Chinese life. With American salaries, we were immensely wealthy compared to the regular population. Most Chinese lived with their multi-generational families in one-room apartments.

In typical Chinese tradition, shoes were to be removed immediately upon entering the apartment foyer. To the left of the entrance, tennis shoes, loafers, and flip-flops lined the wall. I could tell which were Remy's because they looked like kid's-sized shoes.

Directly past the foyer was an opaque glass door to the kitchen, an itty-bitty enclosed square with a door leading to a balcony. The washing machine was located on the balcony, as well as a built-in clothesline. Clothes dryers were scarce in China, so clotheslines were necessary to air-dry laundry.

The kitchen contained a dorm refrigerator, half-sized dishwasher, sink, and an electric sanitizer, almost exactly like the kind used to clean tools between appointments at Asian-American nail salons in the States. In Chinese kitchens, it is used to sanitize dishes after they cycle through the dishwasher because the tap water is not safe to consume.

"Where's the oven?" I asked, looking around the kitchen.

"Chinese do not have ovens," Rune answered quickly.

Large Larry from Lansing cut in. "*Most* Chinese do not have ovens, but some do."

Rune's face contorted in attempted restraint. He did not

like to be challenged.

"Okay, Larry like zero-point-zero-zero-one percent," he said, snottily.

I was confused. "So, how do they bake cookies and stuff if they don't have ovens?" I asked naively.

Rune snorted. "They don't bake, Emily. I told you that we're rich compared to everyone else. They don't have enough money to buy the ingredients needed to make a loaf of bread or *cookies*, of all things." He rolled his eyes. "These people are working all day and night to barely make enough pennies to take care of their families and maintain their shitty one-room shacks. They fucking cook meat with fire because that's the simplest, cheapest way. Do you get it?" He stopped abruptly.

Taken aback by his harsh response, I decided to save my questions for Remy, who had been in China for a few weeks already.

Down the hallway, Remy's bedroom was the first door on the right. His mattress rested on the ground, a lone blanket and pillow atop of a red sheet. The only landline phone for the apartment had been dragged into his room—to talk to his girlfriend until he fell asleep, no doubt—stretching the cord to the max. I wondered how he and his girlfriend would work out their communication schedules, with China twelve hours ahead of St. Louis. I just told Saleem we wouldn't be talking much.

Directly across the hall was Luca's private room. He wouldn't be arriving for a few days but everybody knew his bed was not up for grabs. As our designer, Luca made frequent trips to China to control minute details of the bag creation process.

Knowledgeable in every area of the company, I witnessed how products can be dreamed, believed, designed, manufactured, shipped from one end of the world to another, and marketed and sold through global collaboration. No easy feat, as there were many challenges involved, and Luca bore the brunt of the boots-on-the-ground work in Asia.

He was the backbone of the entire process—traveling by plane, boat, and automobile, hundreds of miles into rural

China every other week to sit in a non-air-conditioned factory, critiquing prototypes to a Chinese seamster who spoke little English. Testing the gear on backcountry adventures in the snowy mountains of Hakuba and dealing with Rune's craziness from halfway around the globe, Luca's distance from St. Louis HQ and proximity to China were both gifts and curses at times.

Rune and Felix shared a room so I could have one to myself. Their view of the Pearl River Delta was out of this world, spanning the entirety of two walls, with a cushioned window seat to take it all in. Felix slept there beneath the stars in a mountain of blankets. I was jealous.

My room was directly across the hall. It was bigger than everyone else's and had an un-cushioned window seat with a cool view. Rune insisted my quarters be furnished upon arrival, so Larry and Remy arranged a platform bed and dresser.

I had my own bathroom, as did Rune and Felix. Remy and Luca shared the hall bath. All three were outfitted with Western toilets, thankfully. The toilets in China ranged from super high-tech to worse than third world, depending on location.

Upscale places boasted one end of the spectrum with futuristic fantasy-land Toto toilets, complete with warming seats, bidets, and more buttons, flashing lights, and Chinese characters than I could ever decipher. Regular Western toilets could be found in most of the newly built high-rises in Zhuhai, but squatting toilets were the norm for mainstream southeastern China. Consisting of a western-looking toilet seat and porcelain bowl installed into the floor, it was necessary to place one leg on either side and literally squat to pee.

If that sounds bad, just wait.

The fourth type of toilets in China, found in older, poorer, and more rural areas, were just straight-up holes in the ground. I have no idea any details on the existence or function of associated plumbing. Often, the holes in the ground were not even afforded privacy. Frequently located in the corner of Chinese factories, if a stall existed, there was never a door.

After we settled in, Rune, Remy, Felix, Large Larry from Lansing, and I gathered in the living room around a purple couch. It was after 1:00 am and I assumed that we would hit the hay. I was wrong. After taking a round of rum shots from our guanxi gifts of liquor, we headed to The Factory, a new expat-owned bar within walking distance from our apartment.

Larry ordered a round of Tsing Tao, traditional local beer, the Bud Light of China, if you will. The bar was absolutely empty, as it was closing down before Larry called to alert them that we were on our way. I could tell Larry considered himself to be a pretty big deal, but I couldn't get a good read on him yet.

After ingesting a sufficient amount of beer, breaking the ice, and busting each other's chops well into the next morning, Rune and I had been awake for who knew how long. Definitely far past twenty-four hours. We were horsing around like drunken teenagers on the walk back to the apartment, dancing and giggling out of control. Felix hoisted Remy up for a piggyback ride while Rune ambled around imitating an Orc from *Lord of the Rings*. He was in his element to the *n*th power.

Zoning out the guys in the background, I gazed out into the sky thousands of miles away from my home—my comfort zone. Mesmerized by the stars and the atmosphere and the unknown, a wave of excitement and serenity flooded over me. I vowed to return to that spot again late at night, alone with my thoughts and the foreign sky.

Back in the apartment, I took a shower and felt refreshed. Checking the time, it was daylight in the States. I thought about calling Saleem, but Remy was on the phone so I decided to get some sleep. Rune repeatedly stated that I could sleep in and come into the office in the afternoon. He obviously didn't know me yet. There was no way I was going to spend most of my first day in China sleeping. I was intent on arriving at the office the next morning whether he liked it or not. Emailing Saleem a brief note saying I had arrived safely and promised to write more soon, I turned out the lights and quickly fell asleep.

My alarm buzzed in my ear what felt like two minutes later.

In reality it was about three hours. I was groggy and tired, struggling to open my eyes. Then I remembered I was in China and popped right out of bed and brushed my teeth. I was told the water was safe to brush my teeth with but *not* to wash dishes with. I didn't understand the logic but didn't question it. I wiped on a few extra layers of deodorant, anticipating the ensuing sweat.

Knotting my highlighted blonde hair atop my head in an attempt to battle humidity-induced curls, I wore a beige lace and royal blue dress. It was cute, but most importantly, it kept me cool in the stifling heat.

New sandals were on my short list of purchases at the Underground Shopping center. Sandstone described it as the Willy Wonka Factory of Chinese shopping markets and Remy promised to take me. I was stoked.

Rune was surprised when I appeared in the living room.

"You're lucky you caught us. I didn't think you would wake up," he said.

"I told you I was coming."

"Well, hurry up," he said. His voice changed to an authoritative tone. "Larry's picking us up downstairs. Remy and Felix are fucking slackers and still sleeping so we'll come back and get them before lunch."

I grabbed my bags and followed him out of the apartment to the elevator, locking the door behind me. Sub-floor one was toasty, beads of sweat forming on my temple immediately. All of a sudden, a huge white van with blacked-out windows and a vinyl Dumbo wrap barreled into the parking garage at a high speed, screeching loudly as the wheels gripped the pavement during the tight left turn. It pulled up in front of us and jerked to a stop. The license plate read 'DBO 420'. Dumbo was a ganja-friendly company. All of the company cars had '420' included in their license plates as well as various iterations of Dumbo and USA.

"We're making a special coffee shop stop today," Larry yelled to the back of the van.

He and Rune made it crystal clear that eating out for

breakfast did not and would not happen all the time. It was purely an introductory nicety for me because it was my very first day in China. They were so over-the-top about the fact that they were doing me a favor, I wished they hadn't even taken me. The two of them together were almost unbearable. Both always wanted to be right, be in charge, and to save face. It was exhausting.

The ride was terrifying. Hundreds of taxis, cars, bicycles, and rickshaws hauling bales of hay and other peculiarities were out and about. Larry drove recklessly at high speeds, darting around vehicles, playing chicken with oncoming traffic.

The bulk of cars were small and compact; most were low quality to begin with and beaten down from battling it out on the roads of China. Chinese driving rules dictated that right of way is dependent upon the size of the vehicle and never to pedestrians. Yielding at any time for anything was liable to cause a hundred-car pileup. It was insane, bringing to mind a quote by the Wu Tang Clan, *driving in China ain't nothing to fuck with*.

Traffic laws exist but are ignored by most. Lanes are painted on the roads but I'm not sure why. Nobody pays any attention to them. Cars constantly weave in and out, forging their own paths, half in one lane and half in another, practicing anarchy in driving form. The traffic signs don't make any sense. Aside from the fact that they were written in Chinese, the ones I thought I understood clearly contradicted themselves.

Larry loved to ignore them all, hooting and hollering, "If it ain't in English, it ain't for me!"

Americans.

Miraculously, we made it through the mayhem to the Dumbo office, located in Zhuhai, Guangdong, China's Free Trade Zone. To the eye, it appeared to be just another industrial park, and was built as such. However, it was subject to special sanctions by the Chinese government and provided favorable tax and customs regulations meant to promote foreign trade and investment. Before the Free Trade Zone,

Zhuhai had been a small fishing village.

Larry parked the 420 van in a gravel parking lot outside of a large cement building located at the end of a long, unevenly paved road. We gathered our things from the van and stepped out into the sun.

A rinky-dink elevator lurched open. It felt like 100° Fahrenheit outside and climbing stairs would only intensify the heat, but I briefly imagined how I would feel being stuck in that tiny death cage while temperatures quickly rose. I chose the stairs. At the top were two large glass doors with Dumbo emblazoned on them. A waist-tall, cowhide drum sat just inside. This was their 'Ring Bell for Service', but Dumbo-style. It was pretty cool. I banged that drum a few times, until the staff got irritated.

The staff lived together in a complex of apartments they affectionately called The Block. A Dumbo 420 van escorted them to and from work where the company chef prepared meals of noodles and mystery meat. The staff ate breakfast and lunch together each day. I would soon join them.

Strategically placed in the middle of everything, Large Larry from Lansing's office was the main attraction of the Dumbo facilities. With concrete floors and glass walls, the "Shark Tank" allowed Larry to oversee his kingdom

Dumbo was not your typical company and their uniqueness permeated not only their license plates, but also their unconventional staff titles, such as Larry's Head Coach, as well as the presence of a massive Ping-Pong table in the basement, where matches fueled by cold bottles of Tsing Tao took place next to the product-engraving station.

The building had no central air conditioning, only a few strategically placed after-market units. We were frying like bacon for an hour while they cranked away, the cool air immediately folding into the thick cloud of heat hanging over the office.

I had gifts for all of the Dumbo employees; it was time to cultivate my guanxi. Gourmet chocolates were my go-to for introductions to regular staff. Scrawling each person's name into my phone to commit to memory later, I played chocolate fairy. Each bag was a little squishy, the filling softening the second I exited the apartment building that morning.

Nonetheless, everyone was in a frenzy over their melting piles of sweetness. Chocolate is rare in certain parts of China. It requires milk to manufacture, which isn't necessarily readily available throughout Asia. Operation Chocolate was a success.

I relied on Sandstone when buying gifts for Dumbo staff, since he knew them personally, like Sally—Larry's Chinese assistant. She wore dowdy ankle-length skirts and button-down blouses in drab colors with her straight black hair tied back in a low ponytail. Black frames covered her eyes. Typically Chinese-reserved, she tended to fade into the background. Trusting Sandstone entirely, I used my Click! credit card to purchase an extra small blue Domo shirt for Sally.

"Domo is my favorite. I can't thank you enough, Emily," Sally kept her eyes lowered, speaking docilely as she clutched the fabric to her chest.

Nigel, Dumbo's IT Director, was about six feet tall, with wavy auburn curls, leprechaun-green eyes, and a crooked English grin. I gifted him new guitar strings, the best ones I could find for the taxing China climate.

"Sandstone told me that your strings weren't doing well. These are supposed to be good for the crazy weather."

"Well aren't you a thoughtful little bugger? I can't wait to try these out," he said, reviewing the packaging with a broad smile. "Thanks, Emily."

I didn't know Large Larry from Lansing or Raheem very well at the time, so I again went with Sandstone's suggestion to gift them fine spirits. Everyone was happy with their largess and subsequently happy with me.

When I first saw Raheem I knew exactly who he was. Among the millions of tiny Asians, Raheem stuck out like a sore thumb. At six-foot-four, he towered over almost everyone except Larry. An expatriate from Mauritius who immigrated to China seeking a better life, he had dark skin, a buzzed haircut, a penchant for marijuana, and an undeniable Mauritian-in-

China attitude. Raheem was in the supply chain business and ruled with a heavy hand.

I wouldn't want to be his subordinate but I'd definitely hire him, especially working in China. He knew how to manage Chinese workers. There is an interesting science involved in doing business with the Chinese. It can be learned, but only through hands-on experience. Raheem had it.

He was a bit standoffish, but I was prepared for his too-cool-for-school persona, thanks to intel from Sandstone. I identified his personality immediately. He was similar to Luca. It was clear it would take a while for him warm up to me, and that would only happen on his terms.

Rune, Larry, Raheem, Nigel, and I marched to the Dumbo van for our journey to lunch. First we had to pick up Felix and Remy from the apartment. Larry sped like a bat out of hell down the roads, chatting about football and barely paying attention as he busted U-turns with no brakes, all while attempting to avoid hundreds of cars doing the same. I death-gripped the safety handles in the van in sheer terror, especially when I had to sit on Felix's lap for the last leg of the trip.

Parking in front of Larry's favorite restaurant, we poured out of the van and our American business was welcomed enthusiastically. The staff was especially intrigued by me. I couldn't pinpoint if it was my white skin, blue eyes, blonde hair, or a combination of all three, but I was a celebrity in China. They flitted around, tittering in Mandarin to each other at a low volume, frequently glancing in my direction and blushing when I noticed them.

After a few minutes, they led us to a large private room in the back of the restaurant. The décor was elaborate, traditional red and gold Chinese decadence from ceiling to floor. It wasn't necessarily the nicest or newest, but I could tell it had been at one time.

We sat at a large round table, with what appeared to be an over-sized, glass Lazy Susan in the middle. Our meals would be served 'family style', where many different dishes are ordered at one time and placed on the Lazy Susan then rotated around for everyone to scoop a lot, or a little, onto their plates.

The number of dishes ordered during one meal can become quite astronomical, and staggering quantities of food are thrown out on a regular basis. The Chinese never like to see an empty plate, or they believe that their guests are still hungry and order more. Hosting, when done by Chinese and others within China, includes showing off your status through excess. Providing guests with more than they could ever consume in one sitting is typical of Chinese hosting.

Large Larry from Lansing was American but his hosting style was one of a Middle Kingdom native. The Lazy Susan overflowed with magnificent dishes, both aesthetically and aromatically satiating. Fish displayed with the head, eyes, and fin attached, and bubbling egg drop soup sat aside bowls of steamed white and fried brown rice peppered with colorful vegetables. Pork and shrimp dumplings were presented in tall, multi-layered bamboo towers. Strange smells surrounded me. Bowls of noodles and green tea abounded. The group ordered a round of Coca-Colas.

"We don't drink soda," Rune said, mostly to the server, but also to me. I looked up with my brow slightly furrowed, straining to keep my lips from forming a frown. I didn't enjoy it when Rune treated me like a child.

"Chá," I said, defeated.

We ate and talked, drinking soup straight from the bowl and slurping noodles Lady and the Tramp style, the norm in China. I struggled with my chopsticks, dropping rice repeatedly.

"Do you need a fork?" Rune asked, pointedly. It was a rhetorical question. He was really asking me how long it was going to take me to get my shit together with the chopsticks.

"Nope, I got this," I said, determined. Focusing on my fine motor skills, I managed to move a good amount of rice from the bowl to my mouth. I swallowed and smiled proudly. He nodded slightly in approval and returned to the group conversation.

Everyone kept mentioning the 3:00 pm knockout, where

typically visitors to China become extremely tired and fall asleep at 3:00 pm the first day. I didn't buy into it until about 3:15 pm. Forcing down texturally displeasing frog eggs at Rune's insistence, a heavy feeling set into my chest. My eyes drooped and I allowed my shoulders to slack, slouching in my chair.

"Tired?" Larry asked me, his devious eyes peering at me with interest.

"See? I told you the 3:00 pm knockout would hit you," Rune said, smirking.

I hated it when he was right about something I was wrong about. Admitting error immediately and taking the heat full-on usually boded well for me with Rune. Time and experience had taught me that he was more likely to forget about it and move on more quickly if he had sufficiently ragged me straight away.

"You were right. I'm super tired all of a sudden," I said, attempting to control a yawn. I was unsuccessful. The table broke out in snickers.

Rune responded in a surprisingly nurturing manner. "You should take a nap, kiddo. We'll drop you off at the apartment on the way back."

I opened my eyes wide and sat straight up in my chair.

"No, I'm ok."

I should have known his concern was just a means to an end.

Rune spoke to me with authority as my boss, "You'll be no good to me if you don't get adjusted to the time difference. Go home and take a nap and we'll pick you up for dinner."

I still had to push back, as I didn't want to seem like a tired little baby girl, unable to work.

"Are you sure?"

"Yes," he said, turning to Larry and instructing him to drop me off at the apartment.

Larry smiled wide and said ok but I could tell he didn't like being told what to do by Rune. He accepted the behavior yet it was suspect. His beady eyes were constantly assessing people and situations, in a calculating, almost sinister manner. Despite the shady stories I had heard about him from Sandstone, Large Larry from Lansing exuded scandal all on his own. I wasn't sure exactly how or why, but I sensed that things were not as they seemed. I had a few weeks to investigate.

Arriving back at the apartment, I found it thrilling to be alone for the first time in a few days. Upon entering the foyer, I unlaced my sandals and pulled my dress over my head, stripping down to my bra and underwear. Grabbing the remote control for the air conditioning, I turned it up to the maximum. An icy fog poured from the overhead unit as I stood underneath it, stretched out. Mist settled onto my body and a chill ran through my spine.

I suddenly remembered my cigarettes. I hadn't smoked one since I met up with Rune before we drove to the St. Louis airport. Fishing around the bottom of my over-packed sling bag, my outstretched fingers came across a scrunched half-pack. I was smart to put a lighter inside. Snatching a bent cigarette and light from the white and green box, I skipped down the hallway to the living room balcony.

After lighting the cigarette, I relaxed into a patio chair and pulled my knees up to my chest. Leaning my head back, I exhaled smoke into the air, watching it dissipate into the Chinese sky. Gazing out over the balcony, I took in a bird's-eye view of a new country and city for the first time. I was very much present in that moment and grateful to be there, although at the time, I had no idea the extent of the impact my travels in Asia and beyond would have on my life.

After finishing my cigarette I snapped a photo of the view. Retreating to my room, I attempted to share it with my friends, but Facebook and other sites are unreachable within the borders of China, blocked by the Chinese government. At that time of day my boyfriend and friends were asleep, leaving me with no one to call. Aside from my communication with Sandstone, who operated on Click's strange twenty-four-hour schedule, I didn't have much connection with the world outside of Asia during my time there, which was fine with me.

I laid down on my red pillow and sheets to rest my eyes for

a second, with no intention of taking a nap. However, I fell fast asleep basking in the bright sunlight.

I was awakened by Remy a few hours later.

"Hey, we're leaving for dinner in like, uh . . . five minutes, Em!" he yelled from the hallway.

Shaking off my nap, I piled into a Dumbo van. Larry, Rune, Felix, Raheem, Remy, Nigel, and I headed out into the street of China, our USA-420 license plate leading the way.

After a few minutes, we veered off the main road onto a downtrodden backstreet teeming with pedestrians. Larry barely slowed down, using the big-vehicles-have-the-right-of-way rule to the fullest extent, nudging against walkers with the van to clear his chosen path. He stopped suddenly in the middle of the street.

"Alright here we are, everybody out!" he yelled like a train conductor. Laying on the horn, he was apathetic to the discomfort of those surrounding the van. The side door slid open and we stepped into mass chaos. Cars zoomed past us, hundreds of people stomped through the streets, taxis crowded the curbs; dingy storefronts, rickety street carts, and freestanding tiki bars littered the block.

Disfigured adults missing eyes and limbs lay strewn across the sidewalk holding cardboard signs scrawled with crude Mandarin characters, pleading for assistance. Groups of poor, homeless Chinese mobbed us, begging the rich white Americans for money. Palm trees were everywhere, a surprising sight. They were transplants.

"Okay, Larry's parking the van and we'll meet you guys at the restaurant. Get a nice table, fuckers," Rune ordered Nigel, Raheem, and Remy. Turning to Felix and myself, he motioned for us to follow him.

"Where are we going?" I asked, not wanting to miss the group dinner.

"Mordor," he joked, in a grave voice. "We're going somewhere secret that they can't go," he continued, with a smirk. Felix and I looked at each other and shrugged.

We followed him down the street, stopping in front of a run-down building that appeared to house a convenience store. Sparkly Hello Kitty cell phone covers, strange meat snacks, Asian brand cigarettes, and newspapers filled with unintelligible Mandarin characters laid atop the dirty glass display case, decorated with water-stained fliers, photos, and talismans. As I peered into the trove of mysterious Chinese knickknacks, I noticed Larry appear in my peripheral vision. He knocked on a door to the right of the case.

A Chinese boy in his early teens appeared and greeted us, "Nǐ hǎo."

"Nǐ hǎo," we responded in unison.

"Nǐ hǎo, wǒmen lái baifang fángzi de zhuren," Larry said. I was always startled when he spoke Chinese, falling for the psychological trick of him being a big fat white American.

The kid seemed to suddenly recognize Larry, quickly opening the door. He bowed slightly while ushering us through one by one.

"Huānyíng huílái. Qǐng jìnlái," he said welcomingly, securing the door behind us.

A thin wall separated the street and storefront from a small room. Inside were two couches on opposite walls, with a large rectangular tea table made of dark wood in the middle, leaving just enough space for us to sit. Tea tables were everywhere in China, not one of them exactly alike. They were all exquisite in their own way.

Taking a seat next to Rune, I still had no idea why we were there. Reverting back to my default state, I began observing details. The ceiling was rather low, composed of white square patches. There was a square missing in the corner and a ladder made of bamboo rested against the wall, disappearing into the obscurity of the attic. I wondered what was up there.

A narrow door led to a compact kitchen even further back in the building. Apparently the storefront masked a miniature row house. I could see a young Chinese girl preparing rice and hear the boy talking in Mandarin to whom I presumed to be his parents. I couldn't understand what he was saying. This was becoming a familiar yet uncomfortable feeling. Not being able to communicate with people could be scary at times.

An older Chinese couple emerged from the kitchen, followed by the boy, then the girl, who I assumed to be his sister. She was carrying a large black teapot. The parents and boy sat on the weathered couch while the young girl placed the teapot on the corner of the tea table, then perched upon a stool off to the side.

Bowing slightly, the elderly man spoke in Chinese and the young boy began translating in English to Larry and Rune.

"Welcome back to our home. We are pleased to host you and your American friends. Please drink a cup of tea in honor of our friendship and the prosperous year of the Dragon."

Lifting the black teapot by a coiled wire handle he began the traditional tea ceremony, sending boiling water cascading from the spout. He followed a clearly ritualized pattern, repeatedly dousing the talisman adorning the tea table in bubbling water before moving to individual tiny tea cups, filling them until they overflowed, steaming shuǐ pouring onto the beautiful bare wooden table.

Chinese tea tables are made to withstand constant water damage and they often have plumbing systems. The seemingly unnecessary act of submersing the teacups in water is done for sanitization purposes. The talisman ritual was done for good luck.

A smaller white porcelain teapot was the next target. After it had been sanitized, the man used a delicate silver scoop to sprinkle dried green tea leaves into the teapot, followed by scalding hot water. The lid was secured and left to brew while introductions were made in Chinese, then translated to English.

The man poured the steeped tea into miniature cups, placing them in front of us. He was *hosting*. As the host, he was the 'big boss' of the house, if you will. The host facilitates the event, and is the prominent point of interaction and decision-making.

He toasted us, "Zhù nǐn tiāntiān kāixīn!"

Everyone took a polite sip from their teacups, fulfilling the cultural expectation. Chinese tea is different from tea normally consumed in the States. I grew up drinking hot black tea with milk and sugar. In China, neither sugar nor milk is added to tea. At any tea table, you will most likely be served Chinese green tea, which has a distinct taste that can be bitter.

The minuscule porcelain teacup had no handle and was scalding hot from the boiling water. Carefully pinching the top edges, I almost dropped it. That would have been awful. Burning myself with hot water, spilling it on their couch, and most importantly, tarnishing the tea ceremony, which would effectively ruin our meeting—whatever it was for. I still didn't know.

As I struggled with my desire to drink the tea and the painful consequences of doing so, business resumed around me. Larry spoke in Chinglish to the man, and the son translated. I didn't know what they were saying, but it sounded like negotiations of some sort. They were going back and forth, auction-style, until the conversation halted.

Silence fell over the room, with everyone watching the older man. He sat very still, in deep contemplation, until he finally looked up at Larry and spoke.

"Shi de." I knew that meant yes.

Larry grinned, his eyes twinkling. "Xièxiè, xièxiè," he thanked the man.

Unzipping the black bag slung over his shoulder, Larry pulled out stacks of American hundreds, piling them on the tea table. I instantly recognized it as the money Rune and I brought over, as they were secured with bright pink rubber bands purchased in St. Louis the day before we left. Ten thousand dollars was the maximum allowed into a country without legal declaration requirements. I hand-carried a bag from the States, filled with at least $10,000 cash, and was told Rune would as well, but there appeared to be substantially more pink rubber-banded hundreds on the table than I was aware of when we departed.

The older man turned to his family and uttered something

in Chinese as he transferred the wads of money from the tea table to their couch. The wife and daughter removed the rubber bands and began meticulously inspecting each bill.

Satisfied with the authenticity of the hundreds, the young boy was instructed to climb the bamboo ladder through the missing ceiling tile and into the attic. Rustling around, he returned moments later with thousands of banded Chinese notes, presenting them to Larry. After shoving a portion in his bag, Larry handed the remainder to Rune, who then passed it to me. Thanking the family, we were on our way to meet the rest of the guys for dinner. I was pretty sure we had just laundered money into China.

After a gluttonous traditional Chinese dinner topped off with shots straight from a bottle of Maotai, scented ricewine that is sixty percent alcohol by volume, we rushed the streets. Splitting into two groups, Larry and Rune retreated to discuss work while Felix, Remy, Nigel, Raheem, and I vanished into the masses.

Exploring outdoor shopping booths, we watched glass blowers create masterpieces and marveled over snacks of cold chicken feet and grilled snake served by street vendors. Stocking up on our fill of music and DVDs at hidden bootleg shops accessible through fake doors, everyone stared at me. To them I was a caricature of the American girl next door, complete with blonde curls and blue eyes. The Chinese furtively captured photos of me from afar, with others approaching to request a snapshot of us side by side. I always obliged, mirroring their double peace signs.

Our next destination was Bar Street, a pedestrian-only avenue where a friend of Dumbo staff owned an outdoor tiki-bar. She was a former prostitute who saved enough money from her gigs with rich white men to start her own business. Although prostitution isn't legal in China, it is ingrained in all class levels of society and a deep-rooted pillar of the economy.

Different levels of prostitution exist in China. Low-end streetwalkers called jinǚ, clad in polyester miniskirts, teetered around on sky-high platforms while working the track on Bar

Street. Intelligent and vocally-talented KTV girls charged hourly to provide engaging company to men during karaoke, open to more if the price was right.

Second girlfriends reside near the top of the pecking order. Men who are in a committed relationship will enter into an agreement to provide financial compensation, either in cash or goods and services, for the exchange of sex and exclusivity of their second girlfriend. This concept seemed to be widely accepted throughout Chinese culture by both men and women.

More often than not, second girlfriends became less of a paid companionship and more of a real relationship, albeit one blossomed from astro-turf, but feelings develop over time, regardless. However, they never lose the all-important foundation of financial security.

Everybody I met from Dumbo had a second girlfriend. Everybody. Traditional obligations to their first girlfriends were fulfilled and a clear separation instituted between the two. The notion of a second girlfriend did not seem to compromise the commitment to or love for their first. Spending time with both the guys' first and second girlfriends, depending upon whose day it was, it became hard to tell which was which. After a while, second girlfriends would seem totally normal. When in China . . .

After a few rounds of drinks, my bladder neared maximum-capacity. The freestanding bar provided no restroom, so Nigel escorted me to a dark back alley where I paid a few RMB to squat over a dirt hole in the ground. I had yet to realize that toilet paper was practically nonexistent in China, never to be found in bathrooms. Shaking dry, I learned the hard way to carry TP on my person at all times. However, flushing paper was strictly prohibited most places, and not recommended anywhere. It was to be deposited in waste cans only. That took a bit of getting used to.

Our night on the town took us from Bar Street to a neighborhood pub. Raheem, Remy, and I snuck outside to smoke a spliff, rolling a mixture of marijuana and tobacco in a loose paper. Taking a drag, I nodded my head in approval to

Raheem.

"Měiwèi!" I said, picking up a word I had learned earlier that day.

"Tasty, huh?" Raheem smiled.

Next up was a dance club blaring techno music. Raheem carefully selected bottles of beer for the group, warning us that "those motherfuckers will sell you anything. Antifreeze, rubbing alcohol, fucking piss. Fake alcohol is everywhere in China." I was glad Raheem was around.

When the club shut down, we slammed our drinks and ducked into a submerged subway staircase descending into an underground karaoke bar. An elderly Chinese man serenaded us with his rendition of Kool & the Gang's 'Celebration' as I grimaced through a shot of Maotai and snacked on watermelon slices and dragon fruit cubes, a far cry from America's popcorn and peanuts bar food.

Around 4:00 am, Nigel threw in the towel for the night. Drunken Felix ran off down the street into a skyscraper, set on exploring. I found him in an elevator headed for the fiftieth floor. Raheem suggested we stop for food and commandeered a large table outside of a bustling Chinese barbecue restaurant that never closed. The time of day or night didn't matter; the streets looked the same. China didn't sleep.

Four- and five-year-old kids immediately ran up to us, tugging at my arm, attempting to hand me roses or strum on a two-stringed makeshift banjo as they sang a song.

"Don't look at them Emily," Raheem said. "Ignore them."

"What? Why?" I asked.

Accustomed to dealing with the homeless in the States, I had never encountered an unaccompanied begging toddler in St. Louis. I learned quickly that no matter how much I wanted to help the kids, I couldn't.

"If you talk to them or pay any attention, they will want all of your money. If you don't give it to them, their pimp will come take it from you," he said gesturing to the shadowy alley nearby, where villains like the one from Slumdog Millionaire hung out. I would only be benefiting a child slave labor ring if I gave them anything. It was tough to ignore them, but if I showed any sign of weakness, they would pounce.

Raheem ordered a fourth-meal feast of epic proportions, fifteen dishes in all: shrimp, dumplings, pork, noodles, beef, squid, broccoli, and more covered the table. And it only cost 300 RMB, about $45 USD. Draining a few more bottles of alcohol, Felix swayed back and forth chasing his spoon unsuccessfully, falling face first into his congee rice porridge.

Raheem invited us to his house for an after-party with fat blunts and white lines but I didn't think it was a great idea. I felt personally responsible for my men. We were all pretty fucked up and had to be at the office in a few short hours. It was nearing 5:00 am. Felix protested, always down for an adventure, but Remy deferred to me as his superior. Not ending his night on our account, Raheem met up with a friend and continued the turn-up.

I had no idea where we were or how to get back to our apartment. Remy manned up and found a cab to get us home. I took advantage of my pretty white American female status and smoked in the non-smoking cab. Nobody tried to stop me.

We visited twenty-four-hour massage parlors at least once per day, often twice. Popping in past midnight for a relaxing foot rub or backbreaking traditional Chinese bodywork, it was completely normal to simply fall asleep afterwards, waking up the next morning on a massage table. My first experience was unforgettable.

Splitting off into gender-separated lockers, young Chinese girls flocked to me chattering in excitement about the blonde-haired, blue-eyed, white American. Eager to assist me with disrobing and showering, their lack of boundaries was startling, unbuttoning my pants, pulling off my undergarments, earnestly ushering me in to the showers and slathering my body in bubbly soap with no hesitation.

I lounged in the Jacuzzi a bit before the girls dressed me in silky spa clothes, holding my shorts as I stepped in one foot at a time then carefully slipping my arms through the sleeves, buttoning each button and straightening the pink collar. Softly caressing my blonde hair in admiration before leading me from the locker room by hand, it was as if I was a regal alien.

In China, massage parlor visits are common settings for business deals, such as golf courses in the USA. Click! and Dumbo staff gathered in a massage room with comfortable recliners, massage tables, and flat-screen TVs. Candles flickered in the corners. Green tea and food were served; noodles, rice, and fruit were strewn about the tables.

Rune ordered two-hour massages for both of us, never missing an opportunity for full-body stress relief. Not realizing this would land me half-naked as my male co-workers received sea salt foot massages, slurped noodles, and sipped hot tea on the other side of the room, I was stuck. I either wanted to work and bond with the guys or not. I couldn't have it both ways, sitting in my own massage room alone.

I entered wearing the pastel two-piece spa wear but needed to be at least topless. I had to take off my shirt in front of a bunch of men I barely knew, and worse yet, worked with. I managed to do so as discretely as possible, squirming around on my stomach with my chest pressed to the massage table as I pulled the shirt over my head. I thought I was in the clear once the massage started but I was wrong.

Girl #56, my masseuse identified by number only, kept inching my shorts down further and further and further until I *just knew* everyone could see my entire butt crack. Chinese massage encompasses much more of the body than western massage, but it was awkward with the men. Pulling them back up a little at a time, Girl #56 laughed and mocked me in Mandarin to the other working girls before yanking them back down again, further than before. I gave up on modesty after that.

Remy, Felix, and I set off to conquer the Zhuhai Underground Shopping Centre one morning, passing the water of the Pearl River Delta on the way. It was dirty brown and overflowing with crabs, dead fish, and a bewildering amount of old boots covered in a gray coating of muck. Descending into the claustrophobic madness of the submerged market, I wasn't prepared for the counterfeit extravaganza that awaited me.

Laid out in a dizzying maze encompassing two levels, shops lined the endless white-tiled hallways, a mind-boggling number of products sardined together covering every single inch of available space, with freestanding booths slinging hot pot wedged in-between throngs of people doing their daily shopping, unfazed by the congestion.

"Come buy, come buy," hundreds of hypnotic voices echoed from hall to hall, their arms and fingers outstretched.

I responded by asking prices for their goods, "Duōshǎo qian?" Then usually, "Tài guì," which meant 'too expensive.'

The Underground was the ultimate place to shop for everything. Clothing, watches, jade, souvenirs, purses, shoes, cell phone cases, and more; you name it, they had it. A fake version of it at least. I was under strict orders from Rune not to purchase any electronics, as the casing may say Sony but the guts would be trash. Everything else was fair game.

Three kids lost in Neverland, we were mesmerized by the circus surrounding us. Gulping bubble tea through thick straws at Remy's suggestion, Felix and I were caught unawares and grossed out by the gummy tapioca balls. Although considered petite in America, I was monstrous compared to tiny Asian girls, barely squeezing into an XXL-sized traditional red and gold qipao dress. Perfecting my bargaining skills, I ended up scoring my favorite and cheapest buy, a pair of electric-blue sandals that I was told passed for Tory Burch. I just liked the color.

Rune was traveling to a meeting in Northeastern China when I ran into problems with the hotel in Macau where our company meeting would be held. Nigel offered to escort me on a desperately needed site visit. The Chinese were difficult to work with, especially since I didn't speak fluent Mandarin, or broken Mandarin, for that matter. My Mandarin skills consisted of about six sentences, and I understood much less than that. I would never get anything done without my boots on the ground, handling it in person.

Nigel and I hopped in his four-door sedan and he drove like a maniac. By the time we parked at the China-Macau border, the right side of my face had smashed against the dirty passenger window at least three times. I sustained a minor shoulder injury and bruised my elbow. Sandstone warned me Nigel was a Chinese driver.

Once in Macau, we took a cab through the global mecca of gambling, home to billionaire poker players who would rather piss underneath the table than leave the game. It has been said that a new casino is built every year, but none compare to the $2.4 billion anchor Macau Venetian, the largest in the world. I had no interest in making any bets, but enjoyed the ocean view once we made it to the outskirts of the city. The waterfront hotel was located on Coloane Island's Hac Sa Beach. I gazed wistfully at the cascading waves hugging the black sand.

"I want to go swimming," I said.

Nigel laughed. "You can't get in the water bugger, too much mercury."

At the hotel, I discovered all things were not as they seemed during my overseas preparation. Rune had yet to be upgraded to a suite, the chocolate the hotel was to arrange had not been procured, and although I thought I was told that Wi-Fi was included in the conference room fee, it was indeed a separate charge.

I suddenly realized my conversation with the hotel staffer had played out quite differently than it seemed.

I asked, "Is Wi-Fi included in the room fee?"

The staffer responded, 'Yes, Wi-Fi."

I interpreted this as, "*Yes,* Wi-Fi." In actuality, it was intended as, "Yes, *Wi-Fi.*" By saying yes, the Chinese are merely acknowledging that they hear you, not necessarily confirming, agreeing, or stating they will take action.

Receiving a false yes was not uncommon; Chinese culture embodies an inherent aversion to confrontation. Neutral acknowledgment in times of disagreement or confusion avoids immediate conflict. In order to survive in the business climate, one must ask the Chinese leading questions, and pose the same inquiry eight different ways. Even then, you can't be sure.

Back in Zhuhai, Rune and I met Larry, his girlfriend, CC, and assistant, Sally, for brunch at UBC Coffee. CC dressed decidedly more stylish than Sally, galumphing around in stilettos and short skirts, flouncing shiny hair as black as her heavy eyeliner.

Rune was in an especially evangelical mood in regards to broadening my culinary horizons. Under his watchful eye and sharp tongue, I consumed whatever dish he set in front of me.

The flat scallion pancakes were tastier than imagined and barbecued pigeon wings surprisingly meaty and flavorful. Little baked cupcakes doodled with decorative icing spirals tricked me, pouring yellow runny egg yolk into my mouth. Shrimp dumplings and lo mein noodles were staples.

I could have done without the rubbery jellyfish salad and pig broth stew, but the vegetable and frog hot pot was the underdog. I went back for seconds and thirds, spitting the frog bones onto my plate in typical Chinese fashion. To wash it down, I was presented a tall glass of room-temperature pulpy orange juice with a chalky aftertaste and a cup of piping hot green tea.

The next day Rune grilled me on the name of the restaurant where we had brunch. I couldn't remember. He refused to let up, hinging his entire perception of my intelligence based on whether or not I remembered the name of this one place I had been to one fucking time during my first trip out of the States.

Focusing solely on my lack of ability to remember every single insignificant detail about everything, Rune fucked with me mentally. Well aware that it bothered me when I failed to solicit satisfaction from him, he often withheld his approval intentionally, testing the limits of how far he could push me.

This is a prime example of Rune's erratic behavior. Nothing else mattered that day. Not the fact that I had managed to finish—within a few hours and while jet-lagged—a fifteen-page report compiled from slacking staff members located around the world, won over most of the Dumbo staff, adjusted to the traditional Chinese food when I had a longstanding adherence to an extremely bland American diet, fixed problems with the Macau meeting, as well as living in a small apartment with four guys I barely knew, relegated to passing each other in the halls covered only by small, China-size towels.

Rune was never satisfied.

We went out for karaoke one night, or as the Chinese call it, KTV. The group consisted of Larry, CC, Raheem, Rune, Remy, Felix, and Luca, who had just arrived in China. Some of our factory connections joined and I acted as host for them.

Larry parked the Dumbo van in an empty lot next to a tall dreary building that gave off a graveyard vibe. Looks can be deceiving, especially in China. Entering through a dingy door, a narrow flight of stairs led us up to a dimly lit lobby. Two Chinese men greeted us.

"Nǐ hǎo." We all responded in unison. As usual, they approached the most Asian-looking person, Remy, and began speaking rapidly.

"Huānyíng lái dào KTV wǒmen hěn gāoxìng néng jie dai ni he ni de pengyou. Nimen jinwan you duo shao ren zai zheli chang ge?" Remy had encountered this many times before.

"No, no, not me. No Chinese," he said in nervous chatter and pointed over to Larry.

The man looked confused, and continued to speak to Remy in Chinese. "Duìbùqǐ, wǒ bù míngbái. Qǐng shuō zhōng wen."

Remy croaked out one of his signature noises, "Ughhhhh, eeeerrrrmmm, I don't know Chinese, man!"

Larry took over, easing through the conversation and impressing the Chinese with his fluency in their mother tongue.

"Wǒmen yǒu dàyuē shíwǔ rén. Wǒmen xīwàng jin wan zu zuì hǎo de KTV fáng hai qing jiwei piaolang de nǚhái."

The two men escorted us up another flight of dusty stairs and into a KTV room. I was awestruck. Leather couches lined the walls. Neon sparkling lights illuminated the ornate design on the tile floor, causing gold-flecked Chinese decorations to glint and shine. Flat-screen TVs were everywhere.

Slices of watermelon and assorted fruits, bottles of fine spirits, drink mixers, and plates of rice, noodles, beef, and Chinese vegetables were presented to us in an assembly line. Since our group included quite a few white Americans, we were treated like royalty all night. In China, we *were* royalty. It was an odd feeling.

A single-file line of Asian women slunk into the room, standing in front of us and posing seductively. A remarkable contrast of East-meets-West, the black-haired girls' clothing choices ranged from stylish red and shimmering gold Chinese qipaos to tacky tube dresses plastered in classic counterfeit Louis Vuitton monogrammed fabric, purchased from the Underground, no doubt. Hair, nails, and makeup were big, French, and caked on. No heel was shorter than five inches.

It reminded me of the famous Bunny Ranch in Las Vegas where upon hearing the bell, girls would make their way to the lobby, appearing in a single-file line-up for the client to make his choice. This was the same for the Chinese KTV girls, except they were being selected to simply accompany us to talk, flirt, and sing.

Renegotiations for additional time and options would take place at the end of the karaoke session, after the would-be johns were sufficiently hooked. Building relationships with the men during karaoke then raising the price for the rest of the night was their business model. It was a smart one.

Rune and I ordered a few girls for the Click! and Dumbo staff, choosing some of the best to gift to our factory connections as an extension of our hosting. Rune kept trying to push a prostitute on me.

"You can have a boy or girl, whatever floats your boat, kiddo," he winked clumsily.

I had zero interest. "Thanks, but no thanks, Rune."

"Emily, you're just scared. You don't know how to loosen up. Just get one for now and see what happens later," he said in a patronizing voice.

Rune could get me to do a lot of things, but accepting a prostitute I didn't want wasn't one of them.

"Really, Rune, I'm good. I have enough people to interact with."

"Whatever. You're a fucking baby. This will be reflected in your performance pay," he said, pivoting and walking away from me.

I didn't give a fuck.

We had a great time at KTV nonetheless. Remy sang shyly, Felix took the mic for a while, and Raheem rocked out all night. The Chinese blew everyone away, seeming to possess a special gene that allowed them to kick ass at karaoke.

When it was time for the mic to be passed to me, I refused. The thought of singing in public made me cringe. I didn't want the attention. All eyes would be on me, critiquing the notes squeaking out of my mouth, a red flush creeping over my body as I experienced a three-and-a-half-minute panic attack. No thank you.

Everybody encouraged me to sing but I just sat quietly, refusing. Smiling with my lips tightly pressed together, I shook my head no, praying Rune wouldn't pick this time as a forced expression of my creativity. He had the tendency to decide how my life should play out, threatening to withhold needed cash if I didn't go along.

If I wanted to receive anywhere near the salary I deserved for the enormous amount of work I did on a daily basis, I would be required to immediately partake in and successfully complete tasks such as accepting a prostitute, participating in Chinese karaoke in front of strangers, eating frogs, or not smoking cigarettes. Yes, there came a time where Rune said he was deducting $500 USD from my performance pay for each cigarette I smoked.

And he called himself a libertarian.

After karaoke, the guys went out with the KTV girls and I rode back to the apartment complex with Larry and CC. Larry invited me in for a nightcap. I could tell he wouldn't take it well if I declined. The elevator dinged as we reached the forty-third floor and I followed Larry down the hallway, removing my shoes before retreating into his man cave. CC remained in the living room.

"I don't allow women in here. You'll be the first, and hopefully, the last," he said, solemnly looking into my eyes. What an odd statement. Momentarily thrown off-center, I realized his sentiment was a calculated attempt to do just that. Larry wasn't the only one who understood sports strategy.

Guiding me to the window seat, I gawked at the skyline, his view ten times better than any in the Click! apartment.

"Phenomenal view, isn't it? Best in the building." He smiled and poured a strong drink.

"Can you make me one of those?" I asked. I could tell Larry wasn't kosher with the fact that I hadn't been drinking like a fish with the guys. I would appease him.

His tone changed to one of a tyrant. "You were gonna get one whether you wanted it or not," he commanded, matter-of-factly.

Even though I anticipated it, I was slightly taken aback by his hostility. Analyzing our positions in the room, they were also deliberate. He rested comfortably in a quilted executive chair behind a stately dark wooden desk, casting a shadow of authority. I was Humpty Dumpty, balanced precariously on the edge of an un-cushioned window seat, my bare feet dangling in the air.

He turned on the satellite radio, filling the room with 70s classic rock. "I love this music," he said, taking a swig of his drink. "Reminds me of home."

"I can dig it," I said, doing the same. It was strong. I was a little uneasy. I took another slug, bigger this time, knowing he was watching me. I didn't want him to think I couldn't handle his stupid drink.

He opened a drawer in his desk and pulled out what appeared to be a jar of crystal-covered kush. I instantly warmed up a bit.

"This is some kush all the way from California. Killer," he

said proudly as he dropped gummy green leaves into the Dumbo-branded grinder.

Displayed on the shelf behind him was a row of glass pipes in a rainbow of colors. He chose a small red one and packed it full, igniting the round bowl until it began to glow like a torch. Inhaling deeply, the pungent aroma of burning marijuana blanketed the room.

Larry passed the pipe to me. As I brought the flame to the bowl, I noticed Larry messing with his phone. We both had the Samsung Galaxy Note, so there wasn't anything he could do on his phone without me knowing. The screen is enormous.

Upon further examination, I realized he opened his Voice Recorder app. Watching as he smushed his Large Finger from Lansing against the screen, he said nothing but I was positive he was now recording our conversation. This was an interesting development.

The slight hint of comfort that I felt upon him introducing ganja into the equation quickly soured once again into suspicion. I didn't know the purpose of his mind games, but I was ready for whatever. Larry was slick but he was no Rune, and neither of them were me.

Pretending not to notice that he was recording our conversation, I activated my learned sociopathic tendencies from Rune and began to play Larry for intel. That's when shit got strange.

"Emily, I like you," he said, speaking slowly, emphasizing each word. "I want to help you."

Not sure where this was going I leaned in, curious.

"First of all, you should know that you look like a fucking idiot with your phone out taking notes. If you need to write everything down to remember it then maybe you aren't cut out for your job."

I was stunned.

"Second, you should be in the background more. Of course you should be seen," he said, ogling me from head to toe and turning my stomach as only creepy men can, "but not heard." I clenched my jaw. "You need to be handling everything for me and Rune, but almost invisibly. You are a pretty girl but you talk too much." Pausing for dramatic effect, he then continued. "You could learn a lot from Sally. She knows her place."

Flames of rage seared my brain but I played along with his charade, expressionless, refusing to produce the response Larry sought.

"Now, as far as Rune, he doesn't know what the fuck he's doing. I've tried to talk to him about a better way of doing business—*my way* of doing business," he said with a smirk, "but he thinks he knows better. And he doesn't." He paused. "I know you have the power. Why don't you just go ahead and do things the way I want them done, and not tell Rune? If you scratch my back, I'll scratch yours," he winked. Larry winked at me countless times that evening. Almost more times than he repulsively leered at me. Almost.

"Click! is run by someone with no formal education—a social worker—and one of my company's rejects," he sneered, his fourth or fifth drink inflating his ego. "In the future, our products will be tagged Click! *by Dumbo*. You need to decide what side of that you want to be on. People who help us get helped in return."

This shit was seriously fucked up. The partnership between Click! and Dumbo was based on the strategy of Dumbo stabilizing Click!'s Asian supply chain—and Click! acquiring Dumbo—never the other way around. Large Larry from Lansing had truly turned Chinese, saying one thing but believing, feeling, and *doing* another entirely. I knew Larry was Smeagol from the get-go; now I understood the intricacies of his plan and would do my best to thwart his attempts at a takeover.

Almost impossibly, the conversation proceeded to become more bizarre and unpleasant. Immediately switching back into friendship mode, Larry presented to me what he declared to be one of his most prized possessions: a photo book of self-portraits gifted to him by CC.

It was particularly meaningful to him because although the Chinese are known to be very indirect, CC had written a heartfelt and private inscription to him inside, which he ironically shared with me. Flipping through the photos, I pretended to care, my mind on high alert for the next kick in the teeth. I didn't have to wait long.

Activating his inner male chauvinist, Larry segued from admiring his girlfriend's caring heart to complaining about her conservative dress and demeanor. Practically drooling, he referenced old modeling photos of mine Rune had shown him. He then tried to coax me into training his female staff how to apply makeup, act flirtatious, and pose seductively.

"People look at you and think sex. My girls need your help," he said with an exaggerated pouty face. "When your work is done," he grinned, "I'll even arrange a professional photo shoot where you and the girls can play dress up and pose as Charlie's Angels. How does that sound?" He spoke to me like I was a mentally handicapped five-year-old, which was probably close to his true perception of women. "I definitely need a photo of Larry's Angels framed on my desk."

I struggled to keep from puking all over his man cave.

Larry clearly didn't know who the fuck he was talking to. It was his intent to break me down and build me up with his chosen psyche but he seemed to forget I was not a submissive Chinese woman. I was an American female, and that shit was not happening.

At the end of our fucked-up conversation, Larry tried to blackmail me.

"You know, we can tell Rune you smoked pot," he said slyly, hesitating for theatrical effect, "or we can *not* tell him." He looked at me suggestively with his shifty eyes. "I think you should join me for a walk with Biraffe tomorrow morning so we can continue our conversation about implementing changes at Click!. Oh, and our plan of action with the girls, of course." He winked again.

So long as I did what he wanted, he wouldn't tell Rune that I smoked pot. He had me fucked up. It wasn't *that* big of a deal to me if Rune knew. I went along with it, not wanting to arise any suspicion until I had talked things over with Rune.

"Cool," I said confidently. He seemed to take my statement at face value. Pretending to check the time on my phone, I said, "Wow! Its late, I better get to bed. We have an early day tomorrow."

Fleeing from the man cave and passing CC fast asleep on their couch, my sandals smacked concrete as I sprinted up fourteen flights of stairs to the Click! apartment, too impatient to wait for the elevator. My fingers flew across the keyboard of my tiny Asia phone, briefing Sandstone on the scandal.

Bursting through the door at 3:00 am, it was midday in Click! world. Felix sat in the living room window seat staring at his laptop and listening to a techno remix of *One Night in Bangkok*, on repeat. Luca was lying on the couch staring at the bright lights on the ceiling, most likely daydreaming about fresh pow or smashing Felix's laptop speakers. The phone cord stretched down the hall underneath Remy's closed door.

Rune's door was closed and the light was off. That meant he was sleeping. He never slept. I didn't care. Tapping insistently on the door until it opened, Rune was clad in only boxers. That was the norm in an apartment full of guys. We had no boundaries.

"Let's go for a walk," I said pensively, ignoring his lack of clothing. He didn't hesitate.

"Okay. I'll be right out." I didn't have to tell him it was important. He knew.

Practicing an art I had learned from Rune himself, I kept my mouth shut until we descended to the lobby, exited the apartment complex, passed the Chinese guards, and were well removed from any possible eavesdroppers.

Ending up at the water's edge, I blurted out, "Okay, Rune, so I smoked pot with Larry."

He looked at me bemused.

"And? Is that all? Is that what you dragged me out here for?"

"No. Of course not."

I spilled my guts, telling him everything that happened that night, beginning with Larry's attempt at psychological fuckery, continuing with his degrading, sexist comments, and ending with his plans for Click! takeover and attempted blackmail. Rune was quite shocked and made me repeat the details over and over again so he could analyze it from every possible angle, unaffected by my personal projections.

"Rune, I know a lot of this shit is new to me. Sometimes I'm not sure about things, and in those instances I don't speak up. But I'm telling you that I'm 100% confident that this is not a positive situation for Click! There is definite misalignment with Dumbo. Larry is fucking Smeagol. I know that for sure," I said with conviction.

He took my warning seriously and contacted HQ to assess how deep we were in with Dumbo. An official report was promised the next day. Rune and I were eager to learn more about Larry's evil scheme so I agreed to go undercover and walk with Larry and Biraffe the next morning as planned. We would act like everything was normal but proceed with caution as we determined our next move.

Passing out in my room at about 5:15 am, my alarm clock awoke me 45 short minutes later. Everybody in the apartment was finally asleep. Gulping a cup of green tea, I remembered that I promised to call Saleem. *Fuck*. I didn't have much time.

The phone was still in Remy's room. Running down the hallway, I twisted the doorknob. Locked. Knocking, I received no response.

"Remy!" My voice was shrill, now pounding on the door with my gavel of a fist. "I need the phone!"

A timid voice floated from underneath the door. "Uhhhh, I have company. . . ."

"What? Just give me the fucking phone, I—wait. What?"

Oh shit. Remy still had the KTV girl in there. You don't let hookers spend the night; Remy *was* a cupcake. I didn't want to deal with that morning-after awkwardness. Forsaking the call to Saleem, I ran to meet Larry in the garden downstairs by the pool.

Walking Biraffe around the manicured grounds of the high-rise, our conversation was more of the same. Except this time,

Larry had a much more condescending tone, overt disdain displayed toward Rune, and list of specific actions to take immediately toward implementing his scandalous plan. He let his guard down, unaware of my tactics of deceit.

After our walk I bid farewell to Larry, expressing fake annoyance at the fact that I had to meet Rune for a private meal instead of joining the team at Dumbo. Walking down the Pearl River Delta to the plaza for our breakfast, I briefed Rune on my conversation with Larry.

Regardless of his outward demeanor, I could see his thoughts swirling faster and faster, the more negative the information I shared. For the rest of the day his brain would function at a reduced capacity, a significant portion devoted to obsessing over the best course of action forward. Ending our conversation, he praised me in an attempted warm voice, awkwardly patting me on the back.

"Good job, kiddo. I'll handle it from here and keep you informed on our next step. We'll keep it all under wraps until we're out of Larry's lair. Have fun with the government and school stuff today." He handed me a wad of RMB. "Here's some extra cash. Live a little." He stood and left, a black cloud hovering above him.

My schedule just so happened to work out to where I didn't need to return to the Dumbo office after my weird interaction with Larry. Rune wanted to play international superhero and build schools in China. I was to make it happen.

Rune arranged a meeting with my first point of contact, a lowly male government official, and it was up to me to take it to the top. Strategically donning a black dress, heels, and mascara to accentuate my blue eyes, I mentally readied my fingers to grip scalding teacups as my driver escorted me in his black Mercedes to the intersection where we would fetch my Mandarin translator, Valerie.

My driver's name was Vic, but that's all I knew. He spoke as much English as I spoke Chinese. We sat at the corner in the idling car taking turns talking at each other. We were obviously feeling the same frustrations and exhibiting identical facial expressions, voice inflection, and body language, but we couldn't overcome the language barrier. We both laughed.

Eventually Valerie showed up. She was delicate in physique, almost like a porcelain doll. Her hair was black and fashionable, with blunt bangs partially covering her eye. We took a long drive to a new city I had never been to before and Vic parked outside of an old gray building with water stains running down the sides.

My point of contact was excited to see me. I presented him with a gift of chocolates and he performed a tea ceremony. We shared cigarettes, as smoking indoors is common in the Chinese workplace, even in government buildings. He delighted at an American cigarette. Charmed by my magic, he introduced me to his boss. This scenario happened again and again until I reached the office of the big boss, AKA the person who could actually get shit done.

My proposal was well received and I was given paperwork to begin an official inquiry regarding our interests in building schools in China. Although it may not seem like much, as a foreigner representing a non-Chinese company, this was considered a victory, especially being a woman working with men. Baby steps.

That weekend, Rune insisted on navigating our way to Coloane Island, Macau for the company meeting although he had no idea where he was going. The two of us were to arrive before the rest of the group so I could have everything prepared. We crossed the border from China then stood around in a deserted parking lot for a while until he realized that we were just standing in a deserted parking lot and not at a stop for a shuttle pick-up.

Having been to Macau a few days prior, I knew we were in the wrong place but there was no way to correct Rune without damaging his ego and causing some type of retribution. I learned long ago to let Rune come to his own conclusions.

He sheepishly apologized, "I'm usually alone the first time I go somewhere. You're experiencing me figuring out how to navigate Macau."

I dismissed it, as everybody gets confused sometimes. But it was interesting and new to see Rune experience a facet of regular humanity, as opposed to being exceptional all the time.

"I don't care man, I'm just enjoying the adventure," I extended the olive branch with a smile.

"That's why I like you, Em," he said, kindly. His uncharacteristic sentiment would repeat itself throughout my life.

Later that day, everyone was settled into their rooms at the hotel, preferred guest points were sorted, and Rune's suite upgraded. I was proud of myself. After all was said and done, the meeting went off without a hitch. Gift bags were well-received, productive marketing and design discussions were held, and guests enjoyed themselves. Yet somehow, one of my easiest tasks completely slipped my mind.

Dinner would be held at Kwun Hoi Heen, one of Macau's best Chinese restaurants, serving artisan dim sum and Cantonese specialties on white tablecloths overlooking sea views of Hac Sa Beach. I forgot to make reservations.

Our party had to be seated at two large round tables, separated by a few feet of burgundy carpet. All of the Chinese speakers sat at one table, leaving me, Rune, Felix, Remy, and Luca at the other. Rune was less than pleased and let me know it.

"This is a serious disappointment, Emily. You fucked up," he said under his breath, but loud enough for Felix, Remy, and Luca to hear. "How can I trust you with important shit if you can't even fucking handle dinner reservations?"

Freezing me out of the rest of the meal, he gave me the silent treatment, pretending not to hear when I spoke to him and talking over my attempts at conversation with the guys.

Never again have I neglected dinner reservations.

After dinner, Rune was really pushing us to go swimming even though the pool had already closed for the night. He really wanted "the kids to have fun." He was only four years older than me, and his insistence on calling me a kid was annoying. However, this time I was grateful. Breaking into the pool with Felix at midnight sounded way more fun than talking business with moody Rune.

Felix and I changed into bathing suits, him in long swim trunks and me in a white string bikini, both of us barefoot. Stocking up on drinks from the bar at last call, we dodged security and stealthily slipped into the pool, splashing around in the moonlight telling stories about life in America and the Netherlands and with Rune.

Caught in the glare of a security flashlight, Felix and I sprinted out of the pool, recklessly climbing up makeshift stairs on the side of the hotel to the roof. Lying flat on the rooftop where the guard couldn't see us, we were soaking wet, out of breath, and doubled over in fits of glee.

"This is super fucking cool, Ems," he said, looking at the sky in amazement.

We gazed at the beautiful backdrop of twinkling stars over the expansive South China Sea.

"Yeah," I smiled broadly, thinking about my life. "It is."

Rune wanted to relax at the hotel for another day so we spent some time working, napping, and playing water basketball. Luca and I teamed up and kicked ass.

Remy complained, "Emily's too aggressive!" Rune agreed with him. They were sore losers.

The guys went out for drinks after dinner, but Rune decided that as senior staff, he and I shouldn't drink with them. He sent the crew off for a fun night on the town and plopped me in a chair at the hotel bar, feeding me wine and refilling my glass every time I took a sip. Not realizing until it was too late, I drank at least two bottles of wine to myself, if not more.

Rune was in full sociopath mode. An information collector, he was trying to get me drunk so I would confess the skeletons in my closet, to use against me at a later date. The night out at KTV had been a tactical move. Click! purchased the prostitute for Remy, but Rune threatened to reveal Remy's infidelity to his girlfriend every time he stepped out of line at work. I may have been shitfaced, but I was still smarter than that.

After closing down the lobby bar, we took the elevator to the balcony of Rune's suite where he uncorked a bottle of red wine from his personal stash, pouring me a tall glass. I was way past my limit and began nodding off during our drunken discussions about Kathleen Hanna's impact on feminism. He finally released me for the evening and I stumbled back to my room.

The next morning my head was banging, and stomach tied in Gordian knots. I couldn't fathom ever leaving my bed but had to check out of the room. Still dressed in my clothes from the night before, I threw sunglasses over my eyes and dragged my luggage down to Rune's suite where I knew his preferred guest status gave him late checkout.

I pounded on the door with all the energy I could summon, wincing and grabbing my head in agony. It opened and I dropped my belongings right within the door.

"Hungover. Need sleep," I mumbled, barreling past Rune to the bed, pulling the covers over me and burying my face in the pillow.

I awoke a few hours later to Rune standing over me in a white robe.

"Good morning, kiddo. Luca and Remy are going downtown if you want to go with."

I definitely wanted to get the fuck out of Rune's bed and go downtown but I felt like shit times a million. Not sure if I could handle it, I rolled over and pushed myself up one arm at a time, rubbing my eyes. I decided to suck it up. I was in Macau, after all.

"I'm going. Tell them to give me ten minutes," I croaked, my voice barely audible.

Rune sent a message on his phone. "They said you have five," he reported back.

My head was in a vice, mouth full of cotton balls, and nausea on level ten. Fumbling toward the bathroom, I caught a glimpse of myself in the mirror. I was looking rough. Oh well.

I tied my hair into a knot atop my head, brushed my teeth, splashed water on my face, and I was ready to go.

Remy, Luca, and I wandered around the narrow cobblestone streets of Macau for hours, walking beneath the Ruins of St. Paul's and admiring the Statue of Guanyin. The juxtaposition of locals living their impoverished lives in dilapidated shacks against the epitome of the excessive billion-dollar gambling culture is how I imagine people feel when they visit Skid Row after a celebrity home tour in Los Angeles.

Unbearable heat and swampy stickiness exacerbated my mega-wine hangover to the point where I thought I was hallucinating. The environment was starting to get to me. Pig, duck, and other unidentified bloody animal carcasses hung in windows of butcher shops. Strange smells of local cuisine— African chicken, Macanese chili shrimp, and po egg tarts— invaded my nostrils. Unusual sights and intimidating crowds of people were at every turn.

I vomited on a street corner in the middle of it all. Remy found me a bottle of water and I took a sip, dumping the rest over my head. I didn't give a fuck. Luca put me in a cab headed back to the hotel. I wouldn't drink wine for a while after that.

I had spent nearly a month in Asia and would begin my passage back to America after a factory visit with Luca and Remy. It was a particularly dark and severe day. The taxi driver loaded my luggage into the trunk under a bevy of menacing gray convective clouds. Rain beat down on the windshield, obstructing the view. Luca took one for the team, buckling himself into the front seat. Remy and I slid into the back. Uneasy about the driving conditions, I nervously tightened my seat belt. Remy reached over and squeezed my hand reassuringly.

Leaving modern civilization, we traveled deep into rural China, staying entertained by the driver's love of K-Pop blaring through the tinny speakers. He played the same song for over an hour. Soon we were all singing along.

Our factory visit was terse, with Luca pointing out multiple product issues and the factory pointing out Click!'s current status of nonpayment. We did not stay for lunch.

The guys were forging on to another supplier but Luca insisted they escort me to the ferry, saving me from navigating the unfamiliar countryside alone. I was grateful for Luca's kindness; it was forty minutes out of their way. Remy unloaded my luggage and hugged me goodbye. Luca waved from the window, not the hugging type.

I double-checked for my passport and stack of Hong Kong Dollars from Rune, then smiled and waved back as they drove off. I would be alone until I made it home. Pulling on my luggage handle, I boarded the ferry and watched the crashing waves from the window as China moved further into the distance.

We docked in Hong Kong before I knew it. Scrambling through the crowds, I managed to lose three of the wheels from my purple rolling suitcase. Great. I had quite the journey ahead of me and would now be literally dragging an overstuffed, seventy-pound purple bag filled with gifts and Click! factory samples around the Hong Kong airport, through the rain on the streets, and into my hotel.

The hotel staff was very kind, arranging a shuttle to take me to the Ladies Market where I could purchase a new suitcase. There was one catch: it closed in thirty minutes. Storing my belongings at the desk, I jumped on the shuttle, practicing English with a Chinese kid as we sat in traffic.

He walked me to a shop where I purchased the biggest purple suitcase I could find, haggling the price down a few HKD. Making my way back to the shuttle, it rolled along empty next to me, soaked in rain and taking up valuable real estate on the overcrowded sidewalks.

Hong Kong was distinctly different from China. Operating as one country under two systems, mainland China's censorship was nowhere to be found. Google and Facebook are accessible and citizens have freedom of speech to a certain extent. Whereas China can be quite dirty, Hong Kong is obsessed with cleanliness, with public escalator handles and doormats sanitized like clockwork. The British influence is strong, cars driving on the left side of the road, Cantonese and English taught in schools, the subway prompting you to "mind the gap" in a European accent. Hong Kong was unique.

My tiny hotel room was barely big enough for the hard bed, which was only 1.5 meters long, my feet hanging off the end all night. The bathroom was smaller than a phone booth and there was no hot water. The hustle and bustle of the foreign city painted a vivid picture loud and clear through the thin walls. I would miss quirky Asia.

I was addicted to traveling. Observing and analyzing the reality of day-to-day life in other countries, I underwent the best kind of education. I couldn't wait for my next trip.

When I awoke the next morning, America was calling my name. Reading a Chinese newspaper on the subway to the Hong Kong airport, I received an email from Rune. He had confronted Larry from Lansing the night before and shit went south fast. The partnership between Click! and Dumbo was effectively terminated. I sighed, validated and happy to have it all behind me.

4 LIFE IS A MARATHON, NOT A SPRINT

There was a big push for Photokina, the largest photography trade show in the world, held in Cologne, Germany. Photokina would be the official debut of Click! and everything had to be top notch, to the tune of a $100K budget. I was assigned with revamping all marketing materials, overseeing a redesign of the entire website, and managing the creation of our trade show booth in Germany—all in addition to my regular duties, of course. I had one month to make it all happen and zero applicable experience.

My relationship with Saleem had fallen into mind-numbing patterns of routine suburbia, more of the same old, same old. Familiar and convenient, but lacking gusto, it felt like what I thought I was supposed to do. My obligation to society.

I had become used to the detached rolling stone lifestyle of traveling businessmen and talked with Saleem about the realities of prolonged periods of separation. We lived in different shades of gray. He said he would wait for me to return. I said I would be gone for a long time. Our conversation ended with don't ask, don't tell.

I was worked to the bone, spending longer-than-usual hours at the office, arriving far before the sun rose and often never leaving. Sandstone had been deployed to China to jump start our new production run. He seemed to be going rogue.

Unreachable by phone, his responses took the shape of brief and infrequent emails. With Sandstone no longer available for Rune to kick around, he turned his full attention to me.

Gone were the days of Rune showering me with gratuitous affection and extraordinary praise, pampering me "like a spoiled American princess," as he liked to say. Something was changing within him. He became less uplifting and more criticizing. His Buddhist façade was beginning to slip.

Sequestering the two of us away from the rest of the staff, he set up shop across the hall in the photography studio. The edge of his desk flush with mine, Rune was in my face 24/7. I did my best to keep up but it was futile. He chose his words carefully, crooked teeth gnashing as he ripped me apart.

"The quality of your work has deteriorated; your focus is lost. It seems like you don't care." He knew that phrase would be devastating to me. It killed me to let him down, even though logic proved his standards to be unreasonable.

Determined to have his hands in everything, Rune flew his old friend Nicky to St. Louis to assist with Photokina projects. Nicky was a Chinese medicine student from California, with bleach-blonde hair feathered over a pronounced widow's peak, and olive-green eyes complementing his rosy cheeks and endearing smile.

Two hoop earrings adorned his ears and a rope necklace made of gemstones tucked underneath his collar gave him away as a sort of a new-age hippie. Nicky performed my first acupuncture treatment, taught me about pressure points to relieve headaches, and gifted me with the universal wisdom of "everything in moderation, including moderation," while telling tales of misadventure with Rune.

Forming a friendship a decade prior, back when no one would have guessed Rune would become a shrewd, high-strung businessman and he was simply a bicycle-riding, rock-climbing Buddhist, Nicky and Rune were now mismatched besties. Nicky was upbeat, genuine, encouraging, understanding, and forgiving. Rune was Rune.

Determined to impress at Photokina, Rune obsessed over

business card designs to Patrick Bateman levels. Daily tweaks were documented in monstrous email chains that circled the globe all hours of the night, with Rune waking people up to over-analyze text size, raised lettering, card consistency, and other trivial details. Although he signed off on the final design, Rune promptly trashed hundreds of bamboo-printed cards when they arrived.

"I changed my mind. I don't like it anymore. We're going with a whole new look and crafting them from metal," he said, throwing a massive wrench into the works. "Nobody else will have metal business cards."

As the stress around Photokina increased, Rune's criticism became relentless and no longer confined to work. My entire life was up for condemnation at any moment. Day in and day out, Rune hurled insults at me, setting elaborate psychological traps, attempting to manipulate me for his own satisfaction.

Devoid of his own emotions, Rune delighted in acting as puppeteer of other's lives. Lips contorted into a sinister closed-mouth smile, his eyes were detached yet joyful as he played God on a regular basis. Somewhere along the way he permanently sold his own empathic being for this evil privilege.

Rune's constant disparaging comments along with my inability to obtain his approval were slowly crushing my soul. He was a loose cannon, his perpetual emotional torture slackening my grip on reality to a dangerous state of disassociation. I was in a nonstop race for control of my sanity, with no end in sight. Rune's thoughts were everywhere, invading my thoughts and dreams and creating my nightmares.

I was a slacker who didn't show up for work until 3:30 am. Other days I was chastised for arriving too early, receiving lectures on life and priorities.

"Life is a marathon, not a sprint, Emily. You should be spending time more with Saleem," he would say.

I was too worried about money. I didn't know enough about life. I could have saved seven dollars purchasing a cheaper flight. My decision to pursue a graduate degree was a waste of time and cash. I wasn't *creative*. My taste in music was terrible. I worked too hard. I didn't work hard enough. My canoe-paddling skills were subpar. I didn't drink enough alcohol. I was throwing away money on health insurance. I should use public transportation. I needed to be nicer to Saleem. My posture wasn't correct. I was naïve and too cynical. I was incapable of relaxing. I needed to take charge. I should be exercising more often. My desk was cluttered. I used too many Post-It Notes. My computer monitor was tilted at the wrong angle. He knew I drank an orange soda the day before.

Rune's tinkering with my brain pushed me to the edge of sanity. I was angry, confused, sad, and alone. Rushing out of the office late one night in a rage after a particularly harrowing day, I emailed Sandstone an off-the-rails cry for help.

He was somewhere in China doing who-knew-what; I hadn't heard from him in weeks. Rune's spiteful behavior and demeaning statements were starting to seep into my mind. It was too much, too often. His derogatory thoughts were beginning to become my own but I knew that was crazy. Sandstone was the only person who could understand. I needed him.

Sandstone wrote me back a brusque reply, listing a few core reminders for survival when dealing with Rune, but little else. His coping mechanism while in St. Louis had been alcohol. Now he had distance. It was clear I was on my own.

I didn't understand the shift in my relationship with Sandstone but knew he had a lot on his plate, and it would be preposterous for me to expect a twenty-two year-old to care much more about a girl halfway across the world that he wasn't sleeping with.

There was no time for self-pity. I put my head down, worked my ass off, and tried to stay out of sight and out of mind. Crashing on the hard black loveseat at the office many nights, I managed to pull it all together before the crew left for the trip. I felt accomplished.

The next morning I awoke in my clothes and spilling off the loveseat. Rune sat across from me sipping green tea from his dirty thermos.

"Fucking slacker. It's after 7:00 am," he snorted.

I wanted to punch him.

"Let's have a quick meeting."

I hadn't even wiped the sleep out of my eyes yet and he dove right in.

"I'm disappointed in you, Emily," he said in a stern voice. "I knew you couldn't do it all. I just wanted you to say it. But you didn't."

Pausing, his eyes twinkled sadistically.

"So you failed. And now I will take over, spending my precious time to fix it all. My hourly rate, approximately five hundred dollars every sixty minutes, will come out of your performance pay." He stopped abruptly, leaving without another word.

We were as prepared for Photokina as we could be. I had no idea what he meant by failing my tasks or him fixing them but I had surpassed my threshold for bullshit and my brain couldn't process any more. I poured myself a cup of green tea as I paired staff members into travel buddies, staggering their flights based upon when they needed to arrive in Cologne.

I had just hired Reid to be Click!'s resident video guy. An outdoorsman, cyclist, skier, kite surfer, and former Olympic rower, Reid was also a creative and smart philosophy major, and beautiful.

Reid's style was hipster-ish, sporting bright-colored skinny corduroys and plaid shirts atop his fit 5'10" frame, complete with suede ankle boots and a mop of curly chestnut brown hair, matching the color of his doughty eyes. Typically Canadian, Reid always had a kind word to share and a smile on his face.

Shipping his extra-large Mac monitors and computer to St. Louis from the Great White North, they traveled in parallel, reuniting at the company apartment he would share with Sandstone, Remy, and a few other Click! staff. His companion for the flight to Germany was Elizabeth, a photographer and the girlfriend of Rune's best friend, Britton. Attending the show as an extra pair of hands, Elizabeth was an acquired taste, so to speak. I wished Reid good luck.

Remy and I journeyed to Europe together. Although he was a good five inches shorter and twenty pounds lighter than me, he insisted on lugging around my carry-ons the entire time, filled with an assortment of chocolates and tea, ten pounds of ginger chews, and over one thousand lens cloths for giveaways at the trade show. My checked luggage was once again stuffed with smuggled Click! product.

I chose to sacrifice my pre-flight time at the airport standing in a check-out line to buy a massive bag of chocolate bars while Remy was smart enough to order a meal. He shared his fried rice and gifted me one of his egg rolls. Squeezing into the middle seat so I could stretch my legs in the aisle, he produced a portable charger when my phone died and supplied ear buds when I came to the devastating realization that mine were still at home. Remy had proven himself a dependable friend and flying companion.

The eight-hour flight was a piece of cake. I did some work on my laptop, watched a few movies, and buckled up for landing at the Frankfurt airport. Next we would catch a train to Cologne, the fourth-largest city in Germany. Packed with more than one million inhabitants, Cologne was a cultural center of the Rhineland.

Navigating the German train station proved to be more difficult than anything Remy and I encountered during our time together in China. We couldn't understand the signs. Everything was in German. Neither of us had been there before and we were dumbfounded.

"Emily, this is kind of cuh-razzzzy. I don't know what's going on here. I'm lost." He looked overwhelmed.

My instincts kicked in and I took charge, leaving him with the bags while I pieced together directions. We made it to the correct wing and descended to our train platform in a crystal glass elevator that resembled the one I read about many years before in *Charlie and the Chocolate Factory*.

Our luggage carrying goods for the trade show—totaling nine bags—rested in a large mound to the side of a bench.

After studying our tickets, I concluded we had about an hour until our train would depart. Remy took this opportunity to roam around and snap some photos of the train station, squinting his eyes and contorting his aim to capture just the right angle.

"Hey, Emilyyyy," Remy called out, "I just heard from some lady that our train is next," he said with concern, his voice slightly higher than usual.

"What? Are you sure? I thought we had at least another half hour." I furrowed my brow and looked up at the digital train schedule marquee, searching for some recognition of German words.

"Ehhhh, I'm not one hundred percent, but she deffffffinitely said our stop, and that it was next." He laughed nervously. "I just don't wanna miss our train. It takes a while to get there."

"Me neither, but now I'm confused."

Ding-ding! Red lights flashed. The train barreled into the station toward us but I wasn't sure if it was our train or not. I looked at the marquee again. It still didn't help. Time was running out. The train screeched to a halt, metal doors bursting open simultaneously to release hundreds of people into the train station.

"Achtung an alle Frankfurt Flughafen Fernbf Passagiere! Der nächste Zug anreisen, ist ein beschleunigtes Bahnlinie mit Zugang bei Limburg, Siegburg und einem Ziel von Cologne," a deep voice boomed over the intercom. I recognized the word Cologne. That was our destination.

"Ehhhhh, what should we do, Emily!?" Remy was freaking out, looking to his boss for direction. I had no idea what to do either. My heart raced. I didn't want to miss our train.

"Fuck it. Let's get on." I yelled to the train conductor, "Hold the door!" Remy and I scrambled to throw our pile of luggage onto the train before it departed. As I fell inside with the last backpack, the doors snapped shut and the train began rolling forward.

After taking our seats, a uniformed staffer wearing a bow

tie strutted through the aisles checking tickets. We handed over our stubs and he scanned them. The black handheld machine beeped angrily. He lectured us in a furious tone.

"Du bist nicht täuschen niemanden, sind diese zweite Klasse Tickets und für die weniger teuren Zug. Ich Schönung Sie zwei und Sie diesen Zug Auto sofort an der nächsten Haltestelle verlassen müssen!"

"I'm sorry, I don't speak German. English only." I felt so stupid every time I said that.

He sighed and rolled his eyes. "You did not pay for this train. You paid for a different train."

So we *were* on the wrong train. I glanced at Remy out of the corner of my eye.

"I see. This is our first time in Germany and we didn't mean to get on the wrong train. Where is this train going?" I asked, concerned.

"These are first-class seats on a high-speed train going to Cologne, and are more expensive. You need to pay more," he said, wagging his little machine at me.

"Okay, no problem! I can do that." I rummaged through my bag, pulling out my Click! credit card. He swiped it and handed me a receipt before moving on.

"That was a close one," Remy said.

"Yeah, I know, right? We could have totally gotten on the wrong train going somewhere absolutely random and not known for hours." I was utterly relieved that was not what actually happened. Lugging around nine overweight bags and Remy, lost was the last thing I wanted to be.

"How much did you have to pay?" he asked.

"I didn't even look." Pulling the receipt out of my wallet, I studied the German writing. "Uh, looks like three hundred euros, I guess," I said, grimacing and wishing that I hadn't known.

"Whoa, that's a lot. Rune might freak out on us. Well, me. I'm the one who said this was our train." Remy sounded worried.

"Don't worry about it dude. We don't have to talk about it.

If it comes up, I'm the one who made the ultimate decision. It's my company card. It has nothing to do with you. I got you." I knew Rune would go easier on me than Remy. Plus, I was already Rune's punching bag; what's taking another hit for a friend?

"Cool. You're the best, Em." Remy smiled, sticking his ear buds in and turning on his iPod.

I settled into my seat, gazing out the window at the landscape flying by. Beautiful, lush green fields and marsh. It looked just like photos of a European countryside I had seen in books, except that it actually *was* a European countryside.

Graffiti, lots of graffiti, covered the train station walls, just like in America. From Frankfurt to Cologne, there were padlocks of all shapes, sizes, and colors secured to fences along the tracks and stations. During stops, Remy and I studied them. Some were engraved with thoughtful inscriptions; others bore names of lovers alongside crudely drawn hearts pierced by arrows. Each had its own story to tell.

Remy captured a few shots of the padlocks while the two of us sat side-by-side on the train snaking through rural Germany. Memories like that are the best. Seemingly small, inconsequential moments are what stay with me the longest.

Hans fetched us from Cologne Central. Dark-haired, slender, and a mile tall, his sharp German features were as pronounced as his accent. The Cologne Cathedral was front and center as we exited, medieval and menacing, and under constant renovation.

We lugged our cargo past a jumble of fourteenth-century historical edifices and modern post-war design structures painted shades resembling pastel produce. Our destination was the corner hotel that would be our command center for the week. Arriving just in time to meet Guus and Chester for a Euro breakfast of fruit, cereal, cheese, yogurt, flaky croissants topped with strawberry jam and accompanied by espresso, we sprawled out on the rooftop of the hotel.

Guus, one of Click's global salesmen and many ski-addicts,

had a strawberry-blonde fauxhawk that fit his bubbly personality perfectly, rounded out by scruff the same color, traditional Nordic features, and bluish-green eyes. Chester was a quirky Englishman expat fluent in Japanese and working Click! sales in Japan. Short, blonde, and supplementing his income as an adjunct professor, he loved hip-hop, loud high tops, and talking. A sick skateboarder, snowboarder, and Beastie fan, we got on well.

Our morning was spent tearing around the narrow streets of Cologne in Guus's SUV picking up flat-screen TVs for the show and performing a run-through at the convention center. Everything was going smoothly despite Rune's dissatisfaction. Returning to the hotel to drop off supplies, we ran into Luca, Benjamin, Reid, and Elizabeth, who had just arrived.

Benjamin was a med student, photographer, surfer, and friend of Felix's from The Hague in the Netherlands. His look was Colonial-Spiccoli, with long curly blonde locks reminiscent of a Whig. He lived across the street from a beach in an office building.

As the only females on the trip, Elizabeth and I were relegated to sharing a room. I hadn't spent much time with her in the past, but knew we were two completely different people. She was about my height and stature, with shiny, longer-than-shoulder-length brown hair always curled to perfection, and moss-green eyes accompanying an out-of-control smile. Elizabeth was overly affectionate, easily excited, susceptible to sudden fits of emotion, and unaware of personal boundaries.

Elizabeth made sure I knew she identified as bisexual, "just in case," she said, winking as she giggled and tried to tickle me. It would be a long fucking trip.

Sandstone arrived at the hotel that afternoon. I hadn't seen him in months. Our relationship was in an odd place. I was elated to reunite with him but unsure of the energy between us.

Grabbing an afternoon snack of Italian cuisine, Sandstone scoffed at my peasantry distaste for sparkling water, or water with gas as Germans refer to it. He was back to his old douchebag state of mind, suffering from 'White Man in China' syndrome, the privileges of which had distorted his ego.

The last slice of pizza disappeared from the pan and our reunion ended with Sandstone voicing his repulsion with my dependence upon Rune's approval and my inability to overcome self-doubt. I heard him loud and clear, but what I really needed was my friend back. Neither of us had the time to deal with the dysfunction in our relationship any further, so I swallowed my emotions and we went on about our day in preparation for the trade show.

The rest of the Click! clan arrived at the hotel later that evening. Gabe, wearing thick black-rimmed glasses, full five o'clock scruffy shadow, and a flat-billed hat, was one of the world's top adventure photographers, and Rune's favorite. He sat in the lobby, cracking jokes, his ultra-dry humor flying over most people's heads. He graduated college a decade prior with a degree in chemistry but more importantly, a love of creating art.

Gabe traveled around the States in a beat-up RV, photographing his friends performing incredible feats of athleticism. He supported himself by selling magic mushrooms until his photography career took off. And it did in a major way.

Next up was Lazar, a Finnish dude with long, filthy hair, cleft chin, and rugged face. He was willing to do *anything* to get the shot. I'm talking scaffolding to the peak of a snow-covered mountain in the dead of winter with an ice pick. Arvin, a kindhearted, blonde-haired German with a permanent glowing smile, was famous for his trippy time-lapse shots of BMX bikers. Two ski photographers from France arrived as walking caricatures, bearing berets, twisty mustaches, and silly grins. The caliber of creativity that surrounded me had no choice but to be life-altering.

That night the Click! crew went out for laughter, grub, and beer. Overflowing from two large tables on the promenade, we dined al fresco. A round of Kölsch beer was delivered to the table by a beautiful smiling German woman who took our orders for a bevy of traditional dishes to share.

I paid our exceptionally large tab and we headed to a local pub where Jäger shots were the drink of choice for everyone except me. I chose something less potent. Someone had to be responsible for the show in the morning.

Bar hopping from dive to dive, our group dwindled to a few. Partying in the hotel lobby at the end of the night, Sandstone and I stole away for a few minutes, picking up our earlier conversation while smoking on the stone corner beneath the neon lights of the hotel. By this time we had both imbibed in a few drinks. I wanted the truth about why he was so disgusted with me. I demanded it.

He didn't hold any punches.

"You're just Rune's yes girl, his bitch. That's what you are, Emily. That's what I was, but not anymore. I've had a lot of time to think in China—away from Rune. Now you need to think for yourself, stop being so fucking weak. You're not a weak-minded person but for some reason you let Rune control you. He's not always right, he's not fucking God." His words were dripping with repugnance.

"Yeah, easy for you to say, Sandstone. You're eight thousand miles away." My voice was bitter. "Rune's been on my fucking dick every minute of every motherfucking day for the past month, criticizing every move I make. You know me. You know I can't handle that shit. I don't deserve that shit."

"Emily, I know. But we both know how Rune is. You've gotta man up. You can't let him destroy you. He's trying to fuck with you and you're letting him. You're smarter than that; you're stronger than that. Man the fuck up." Looking me in the eyes, he spoke deliberately. "Be your own person."

Although we both suffered from Stockholm Syndrome to a certain degree, there was no denying the fact that he was completely right. Somehow we drunkenly called a truce and hugged. I felt much better with Sandstone back on my side, but had a lot of thinking to do. Sandstone said a mouthful and Rune's treatment of me the past month confirmed it all. But first I had to get through Photokina.

The Photokina trade show was both exhilarating and exhausting. Each morning was a 5:00 am wake up and breakfast with the team, everyone hungover and falling asleep in their eggs. We hauled the day's goods to the Neumarket station by foot, where we caught the tram to the convention center—one last moment of relaxation before the madness of the show began.

We were on our feet all day, setting up and closing down, talking, smiling, laughing, selling. Entertaining high-profile names from the industry, we hung out with the world's most creative people. Remy and I tag-teamed the Red Bull reps, finessing contest sponsorship terms. Harrison, Click's top-secret new marketing guru, stopped by for brief introductions and once-over of the booth before jetting off to Munich on personal business.

Nicky flew over to be our suit-clad barista, a tea connoisseur if there ever was one. Giving away a steaming cup of Oolong Tea to trade show attendees was a brilliant idea of Rune's. The line wrapped around our booth. We also had a troupe of gorgeous European models adorned in Click! tank tops flitting about the show, leading a trail of entranced men directly to us. Rune and I were pretty smart.

Each day I chose between a butter-and-spinach sandwich or plain bockwurst and baguette for lunch, with either a Coca-Cola or Kölsch beer. Drinking beer before noon was normal in Cologne. After day one I gave up on fancy stilettos, instead buying comfy beige booties to pair with dresses. Rune approved.

"You look very European."

After dinner in the evenings I declined offers to go out partying with the staff. Preferring to recuperate and recharge alone in my room after such a draining day, I packed Click! giveaway bags. One night, Nicky offered an acupuncture session. Lying on a towel on the floor, my body was poked with tiny razor-sharp needles. It was a painless procedure that boosted my energy tenfold after a hectic day.

As the week of the trade show winded down, after-parties started popping up. Click! staff attended bearing gallons of homemade sangria to share. We *were* the party. In lieu of a glass of wine, I sipped an espresso. There was still one more day left of the show and I was determined to reach the end on-point. I didn't suffer through eighty-hour hell weeks and a nervous breakdown to fuck off at the actual event. As second-in-command, I knew how to have fun and *when* to have fun.

The lobby was a madhouse when we returned to the hotel. Everyone was beyond wasted and a few drag queens were peppered throughout the mix. Gallons of Click! sangria had been consumed, countless beer, and at least three bottles of Jägermeister.

The alcohol tolerance levels of the crew were mixed. Starting with the exceptional, Hans was full-blooded German and could drink everyone under the table with ease, popping up bright-eyed in the morning, high energy and ready for the day. The Dutchies, Felix and Benjamin, were similar. Others couldn't keep up. If they drank at night they were train wrecks in the morning, late to breakfast—if they made it at all—eyes puffy, barely open, their words sparse and voices cracking.

Some of the staff was passed out on the couch, others were laughing hysterically, a few were dancing, and a small group huddled together outside smoking hashish. I hung around for a few moments but once they started drinking Jäger from the butt of a plastic crow, I knew it was time for me to go to bed. I had no idea where the plastic crow even came from.

Apparently, it was from the same establishment as the fire extinguisher Felix liberated earlier that evening. Around 2:00 am, Felix decided to extinguish the entire neighborhood, walking down the streets, spraying cars with white smog, looking like a Ghostbuster. A concerned citizen called the cops, who set out on a manhunt for the fire extinguisher bandit. Felix fled into the night, dumping the evidence someplace only he knew.

Nicky went to Rune for help, who upon waking at 2:00 am did three things. First, he asked where I was. Nicky informed him I was asleep in bed. Second, Rune stated he didn't care if Felix was arrested. Third, he went back to sleep. I was filled in over breakfast.

"Rune, when they started drinking from the butt of the plastic crow, I knew it was time for me to go to bed." We both laughed.

"Emily, I never questioned your involvement."

I beamed, glowing from what I considered praise from Rune. I was happy Rune knew I was responsible. He spent the entire trip ragging me for not going out drinking with the crew every night, saying I didn't know how to have fun. It paid off once.

Getting everyone to the train station on time was a challenge. Remy puked in a trashcan on a street corner. Yes, I had done this recently in Macau, but not on a workday and especially not during a trade show. I cut him some slack, instructing the group to continue on. Buying him a bottle of water from the Döner Kebab stand, I hoisted his bags onto my already-strained shoulders until he felt ready to carry them again.

Remy was noticeably off that day, his less-than-stellar exchanges catching the eye of Rune, who ordered me to dock his performance pay by three thousand dollars. I conveniently forgot. Remy had been a good friend. I tried my best to return the favor. I often did this for Click! staff, attempting to shield them from Rune's senseless acts of malice.

In the end, we kicked ass at Photokina. It was almost perfect, especially considering the majority of our staff's (lack of) trade show experience and jet lag. Our hard work paid off and I was more than proud of myself and my team. Rune of course pulled me aside to burst my bubble, nit-picking the staff's performance to death before we even had a minute to reflect. Par for the course.

Everybody had been bugging me to party with them all week, but most were too hungover to make it out the last night. Luca, Gabe, Elizabeth, Chester, Sandstone, Reid, and a few others managed to find some energy. A Foosball bar was our after-dinner entertainment.

Joining the masses of pedestrians on the streets, we were a raucous bunch. The sidewalks on our path were quite narrow, due to the bike lane, so our group formed a double-file line. Luca and I walked side by side.

The unmistakable smell of patchouli engulfed us without warning and a head shop appeared on our right. Somehow the conversation turned to MDMA.

"Drugs are bad. You shouldn't do them," Luca said.

I rolled my eyes. "Whatever, Luca. I don't even do drugs for real, I just smoke weed. But I've been following research on MDMA and studies have proven side effects to be minimal and not permanent. I want to try it."

"I've done it before. It felt great. But then one day I went out on my snowboard and I was flying through the air, I don't even remember what I was doing, eh, trying a flip or something, I don't know, but what I'm saying is, with fresh pow under my board out there in the mountains, I felt that same feeling—but better. It was fucking sick." Luca stopped and looked at me. "Moral of the story: you can achieve the same emotions through living like a champ."

Never underestimating the wisdom exchanged during spontaneous conversation, I mused over his sentiment long after that night in Cologne. I wanted to discover and create my ecstasy on demand.

Furchtbar, which means 'terrible' in English, was threadbare and grungy, bragging indie music as well as the best Foosball tables in Cologne. My team with Gabe lost two games in a row, knocking us out of the tournament. I taught the bartender how to make cherry bombs and Elizabeth's iPhone was stolen, sending her back to the hotel in tears, escorted by Chester.

Alone on bar stools at a tall table, Gabe and I high-fived our epic Foosball failure before downing shots of flavored vodka. The professional takeaway from our conversation was both simple and paramount.

"People work with people they like that are fun to be

around. Period. If you're a dick, it doesn't matter how good you are at what you do. They'll hire the fun, nice guy." Patting my arm reassuringly, he smiled. "Don't worry, people like you. You're fun."

Bonding over a mutual fondness for American politics, classic old-school underground hip-hop, and world travel, we understood each other on another level as well.

"My girlfriend wants a baby. I travel so much for work I can't even have a dog," he lamented.

"Yeah, I have no plans anytime soon to up and quit my life for nine months and have a baby," I agreed. Neither of us wanted to give up our careers for our home lives. We were in the same boat and had company. Reid paddled alongside us through a pool of his own girlfriend issues, standing in the corner of the bar in deep discussion with his love on the phone. He would break up with her within a few weeks, his personal life already tallying victims to his budding film career.

Gabe, Luca, Sandstone, Reid, and I staggered back to the hotel at about 2:00 am.

"There's a bunch of cops over there. Don't do anything stupid, guys," Gabe said right before we walked across an empty intersection.

A loud whistle blew, stopping us in our tracks. The German police detained us for jaywalking. They asked if we were from Europe. Our answers were a jumbled mix of "Japan," "Canada," "USA," and Sandstone's drunken "'Murica." Of course Sandstone had to continue with his big twenty-two-year-old mouth and shit on their laws, spitting while he spewed belligerently.

"In 'Murica, I could argue in a court of law that since the streets are empty and its late, there was no imminent danger, technically we weren't in the wrong . . ."

"Ahh, shit," I muttered.

We all groaned and Gabe elbowed Sandstone in the ribs. Antagonizing the Cologne Polizei was the worst strategy for us at this point. I needed to be on a plane in a few hours and didn't have time to be arrested. After some back and forth, it was discovered that none of us were carrying our passports. This fact—and the resulting paperwork for the police—ultimately saved us. We were released with a warning and jubilantly continued back to the hotel.

It was chaos. We were all drunk. I still had to arrange Reid's flights for his backcountry shoot with Gabe in Chamonix, France, the next day. Gabe and I ran down the stairs to his room and had the trip itinerary planned and tickets purchased by 3:30 am.

Gabe and I sat on the floor poring over unbelievable shots from his recent trip to Greece, humming along to Jurassic 5, and feverishly debating politics. His eyes were deep and dark but far from empty. The mind behind them was artistic and analytical. He was purposefully aloof, observing—not shy. Gabe was his own person.

"I haven't seen you out much this week," he said, noting my absence at the bars.

"Yeah, I've been really focused on work. I mean—that's why I'm here, right? I put in a lot of time preparing for PK. Somebody's gotta be focused and execute, you know?" My tone was matter-of-fact.

Gabe nodded. "I'm the same way when I'm working. I understand that. I respect that." His words, some of my favorites, echoed around the now seemingly very empty room. "Rune's fucking crazy. I know you've been under a lot of stress dealing with that bullshit."

He moved to the bed behind me and began to massage my knotted shoulders. I relaxed for the first time in months and made the executive decision to sleep with him.

Kicking off my shoes and joining him on his bed, he kissed my lips. Gabe stripped me down to my black lace boy shorts, then took off his royal blue button-down and cuffed black denim jeans.

"Wait—do you have a condom?" I asked, not willing to go any further without one.

"Yes." He ran over to his bag and retrieved the square plastic wrapper.

Pulling my hair with one hand, he slapped my ass hard. I wasn't expecting that from Gabe. He bit me, and not too gently. He was full of surprises.

It felt deliciously scandalous. I didn't think of Saleem.

Gabe ran his fingers up and down the curves of my naked body. I looked at the time, realizing I had fifteen minutes to pack and be in a cab with Remy on the way to the train station.

"Oh shit, I gotta go," I said, hastily pulling on my jeans and tank top. "It was fun." I smiled.

"Do you want me to help you pack?" he asked, concerned and grabbing for his shoes.

"Nope, I got it. Thanks for offering though. Get some sleep." I winked and shut the door behind me, running for the stairs.

Our room looked like a tornado hit it. Elizabeth was already gone on an earlier flight and left stuff everywhere. I threw clothes and personal belongings into my big purple suitcase, sitting on top to zip it shut, not caring what was smashed. Abandoning everything else in the room, I ran down the stairs through the front door. It was still dark.

Remy was standing in the flashing hazard lights of the taxi while the driver loaded his bag in the trunk. I threw mine down on the ground and smiled, breathing heavily.

"Em! I didn't think you were coming! I looked for you but you weren't in your room. I thought you got taken, dude!" he was serious, his voice concerned.

"Aww, no, Remy I didn't get taken," I laughed, smiling hard. "I'm here!" I said happily. "Let's go back to America!" We hopped in the backseat.

The taxi sputtered to a start and took off down the uneven cobblestone. Whipping my head around, I watched the hotel as it faded into the early morning European darkness. I felt accomplished. If I could make it through Photokina, I could make it through anything.

Rune was right. Life is a marathon, not a sprint. I had just successfully completed the first leg.

PART II
THE END

5 MEGA-ASIA ADVENTURE

Back in St. Louis, the Click! staff savored our Photokina success for weeks. We rocked it and did it as a team. My spirit was renewed, ready for the next challenge. I spent even more time working.

I spared Saleem the details of my infidelity in Germany, keeping with our agreed upon stance of don't ask, don't tell. Saleem and I barely saw each other anymore anyway. He didn't seem to notice, passing his days Frisbee golfing and nights playing poker at the bar. Saleem never doted on me too extravagantly, but it was now reaching a point of neglect. It appeared to make little difference to him whether I was in the country or not.

We discussed him seeking better employment to lessen my financial burden and stress, but he never got around to completing an application in its entirety. I wasn't going to do it for him. I had enough to worry about.

Rune decided he wanted to be more visible in the political sphere. We were invited by a global trade organization to join twenty high-profile individuals from Missouri businesses, universities, and government on a delegation trip to China. The jam-packed itinerary would take us to Hangzhou, Beijing, Nanjing, and Shanghai.

When the delegation trip concluded, Rune and I would jet

over to Macau for our bi-annual company meeting. Topping off the mega-Asia adventure, the two of us would then spend a week in Thailand for vacation, hitting Shenzhen before and Hong Kong after. It seemed like a good idea at the time.

Rune considered my invitation for this trip to be a privilege. I did too. It's not every day I'm given the opportunity to be peers with senators or carted off to Thailand for holiday. I recognized that I was extremely lucky, especially when Rune told me repeatedly how much my plane ticket to Thailand cost.

"Remember, I'm using my own *personal* money to buy your ticket, not *Click!*'s."

This was humorous, considering his entire life was funded from Click!'s bank accounts. He refused to accept payment from me, so his self-aggrandizing behavior was just bullshit in order for him to feel good about himself. I was sure he planned to deduct it from my next performance pay anyway, but couldn't prove it.

Rune left for China a few days before my departure. At this point, I was comfortable traveling alone. I preferred solitude over spending hours strapped into a chair next to Rune, forcing laughter at his unfunny jokes and smiling when I wanted to scowl.

After tediously packing enough professional outfits and underwear for a month-plus, I boarded my seventeen-hour flight to Shanghai, taking a two-seat section by the window. Settling in with a blanket and pillow, I washed down a sleeping pill with bottled water and pulled out a stack of Chinese thank-you cards to work on until the drowsiness kicked in.

I crafted fifty thank-you notes for each important person we would meet on the trip. Cultural competency in China had been a focus of mine over the past year. My cards were red, the universal color of luck in China, referenced the much-revered Chinese New Year of the Dragon, and included a heartfelt message composed entirely of handwritten Chinese characters.

Each Chinese character is composed of multiple strokes, and each stroke has a set order to follow. The Chinese can tell if the strokes were written out of order. This may seem like an extreme eye for detail, but English speakers can relate by considering the visible difference between someone writing an O beginning from the top and continuing counterclockwise, as opposed to someone writing an O beginning from the bottom and continuing clockwise. Same idea; it doesn't look right.

Each Chinese character conveys something, a person, place, or event, that when combined together, paint a descriptive picture. This is why Chinese doesn't correctly translate to English literally. Their characters are less 'words' and more 'ideas,' aided by cultural connotations.

Bored to tears and exhausted beyond belief when the plane touched down at Shanghai Pudong International Airport, I cleared customs and peered into the crowd of people at arrivals, searching for a sign with my name. There it was, Emily Carpenter, Click!. The hotel was a two-hour drive in the evening darkness from the airport.

Meeting Rune and a few others for midnight drinks in the hotel penthouse, I was among good company. The Governor's Chief of Staff sat to my left, and former Presidential administration staffers to my right. Introductions were made, Hendricks's gin and tonics stirred, jokes told. I was the youngest person in the delegation by far—the only one in their twenties—and one of two females.

The trip was insane in the best and worst ways. Experiencing the big cities of China on a luxury tour was quite different from my time in Zhuhai. Continuing his schizophrenic ways, Rune insisted I take his upgraded chambers at each stop. I dozed on what should have been his king bed in an oasis of silky sheets, fluffy pillows, and down cushioning. Bathing in steaming rainforest showers and bubble baths in deep, round tubs enjoying the glass-walled view of each city, I knew it would come back to fuck me somehow.

Our delegation followed a structured itinerary of work and fun from early morning to late night. We tiptoed through the ominously quiet, world-famous Jade Buddha temple among twenty-foot-tall mystical deities, purchased best-of-the-best Super Long Jing loose leaf to bring home from elaborate tea tastings, and traded RMB for silk scarves at the center of China's fashion industry, Nanjing Liu, known as China's No. 1 Street. Riding the dizzying elevator 474 meters to the top of the Shanghai World Financial Center Observation deck, I stood on the clear glass floor taking in a view like none other with fear and excitement in my eyes.

We stretched our taste buds with spicy Yunnan cuisine at Lost Heaven, a restaurant located on Shanghai's iconic waterfront, Zhongshan Dong Yi Lu. Speeding across China's rural countryside in the comfort of the Bullet Train's first class seats, Rune insisted we indulge in high tea and biscuits upon checking into the Ritz-Carlton.

I sported smart pantsuits and elegant dresses, danced to the Missouri Waltz with Chinese Party officials, and drank more gin and tonics than anyone probably should. The refined Beijing Hong Kong Jockey Club was the location for our dinner with a bank president who had over $3 trillion USD to invest. He loved my gift of gourmet chocolates.

Three duck carvings were performed, the preparers wearing chef's whities. Maotai toasts were never ending. I smiled and cheered "gan bei," which is a common toasting phrase in China that means 'dry the cup,' but secretly drank water when the president requested we share a special third shot of Maotai.

Rune was insufferable. Three days before our trip, he decided he would be a vegetarian that month, forcing the organizers to make last-minute accommodations. After all that, I had to hide the fact that he was eating bacon "for protein" at breakfast every morning.

He refused to participate in most of the delegation activities, which made him look like even more of a dick than usual, but worked in my favor. Any event he backed out of, I saved the day and represented Click! as a warmer, kinder, more engaging version of Rune.

I would have been in attendance regardless, but being perceived as someone's assistant, relegated to standing room in the back is an entirely different experience than being escorted to the big chair in front and recognized by important people as someone of importance. Especially in China, where status is everything.

I experienced life light years of levels beyond my own membership. My day-to-day was a whirlwind, planning future swimming trips to the Mississippi River with the Chinese equivalent of the Secretary of State, experiencing the lockdown security of the United States Beijing Embassy where I met the US Ambassador to China, attending conferences with the VPs of Amazon and FedEx, meetings with Foreign Investment Development Boards, lunch with the presidents of respected universities, and lavish dinners with multimillion dollar corporations. Not to mention the fact that I was traveling with a state senator.

Professionally, the trip was going better than I could have imagined. Each time I presented myself as someone of significance, I believed it more and more. Every interaction boosted my confidence, adding another layer to my self-worth. I learned that political leaders and CEOs and billionaires were all just regular people. I could be them too. My possibilities were expanding.

It wasn't without great sacrifice. All things Rune-related have a dark underbelly. The rosier the presentation to the public the grimier things were behind closed doors. It was akin to an abusive relationship. I was walking on eggshells, staying close enough to the delegation group to dissuade his unscrupulous behavior, but far enough away to where I could quickly step out of their earshot if he began to lash out. In private, I was slinking around in the shadows, hoping not to be seen.

Rune had changed completely from when we first met. Increasingly image-obsessed and power hungry, he rotted from the inside out, becoming everything he said he was not. On a quest to demonstrate clout, he put me down to bring himself up every chance he got. It started before Photokina and progressively worsened, unleashing a new level of sadism.

Rune invited me to join him on this trip. We peddled our bibles to widows as a team. It was clear that he needed me as a buffer between his cold, abrasive persona and the rest of the group. Pushing me into the spotlight, he forced me to stand in for him and assert that I was Someone.

When people took me seriously or I received praise or attention from anyone, he would immediately intervene, cutting me down to size publicly for dramatic effect. Insulting me outright, purposefully forcing me to perform ridiculous, meaningless tasks in order to embarrass myself in front of the delegation, proving that *he* was the all-important big boss, Head Dick in Charge—lest anyone forget. His behavior was bizarre and erratic. I was concerned for his mental state.

The evening we arrived in Beijing, Click! hosted a get-together in Rune's hotel suite. The group assembled, gin and tonics with the perfect ratio of ice-to-Hendrick's were poured, and Rune's weird robot music played in the background. The group burst into laughter as I delivered the punchline to a joke. Rune sat on a bar stool alone, looking surly.

"Emily," he barked. "I need more minutes for my Asia phone. You need to go get a top-up now."

It was 12:45 am. I looked over with a slight hint of disbelief in my eyes before quickly fixing them. I didn't need him going off the deep end in front of everyone.

"Okay," I affirmed. I turned to the guests, apologized and excused myself.

With a face burning bright as a Christmas light, I retrieved my bag from the bedroom. Not only was I mortified; I was about to be extremely cold. Rune knew full well that I stupidly did not bring a coat with me. It had been the topic of discussion from the moment we stepped off the train.

It was momentously colder in Beijing than our previous city, but Rune denied me his extra coat for the duration of the trip.

"That will teach you a lesson you won't forget."

Men in the group offered to retrieve the top-up for me while others expressed concern for my safety. Someone presented me with a coat. I wanted to take it but knew I couldn't. I smiled at them awkwardly as Rune looked on, waiting for me to misstep. I wouldn't give him the opportunity to flame me in front of them. I acted exactly as he wished.

"She's a big girl. She'll be fine." Rune said in a stern voice, ordering me along.

Swallowing my pride, I exited the suite, taking refuge in the hallway. I felt like an idiot.

What the fuck was my life?

I signed on to pay my dues and no one could say I hadn't done that. I put up with his poor treatment because it was better than no opportunities, and I didn't really have the luxury of a breakdown at the moment. There was a mission at hand to complete or there would be hell to pay. Who was I kidding, there would be hell to pay regardless, but returning with a top-up might lessen it a bit.

I braced myself for the cold and marched out into the quiet darkness, illuminated only by streetlight. The biting wind slapped my face and I began shivering. I'd only been in the city for an hour or two and knew nothing about Beijing. I felt like Rune sent me on a wild goose chase to punish me for something, maybe for people liking me. But I wouldn't be thwarted that easily.

The party was over by the time I returned. Rune was watching TV on his tablet. My lips purple from the cold and hands bright red, I presented him with the top-up. He didn't take it or look at me.

"I don't need it anymore," he said nonchalantly, never breaking his gaze from the tablet.

Smoke poured from my ears. *What a fucking douche*. I dropped the top-up on the coffee table and locked myself in my bedroom, plopping down on the ten-layer mattress and wrapping the billion-thread count sheets around me to warm my frostbitten skin.

I was exhausted, mentally and physically. We still had a few more weeks to go. I didn't know if I would make it.

Without warning, I was his best friend again. When it was bad, it was terrible. But when it was good, it was out of this world. Rune was excessively nice, his entire demeanor changing in an instant. He surprised me with late-night trips to exquisite massage parlors, gifted me candied confections, ordered me to sleep late and arranged delivery of American breakfast in bed; I never knew which Rune I would encounter until I saw it in his eyes.

This was nothing new but Rune was losing control. Suddenly incapable of maintaining an internal balance, he careened from one extreme of the moral spectrum to another, resorting to desperate measures for damage control.

On our way to a fancy dinner one night we passed a group of luxury boutiques. I lingered over a pair of red-bottomed five-inch stilettos sparkling in the gleaming lights.

"Do you want them?" Rune asked.

"Hell no, dude. You know how much those cost?"

"Yes. You work hard. You deserve it." He moved toward the door, glancing at the hours. "They're still open. Come on kiddo, let's get you some Louboutins," he smiled and motioned for me to follow him inside.

"Thanks but no thanks, Rune. You know I have fucked-up knees from playing soccer. I'd probably wear those like once or twice—actually, I wouldn't even want to wear them. I can't justify spending that much money on shoes," I said defiantly.

I meant it. Louboutins meant nothing to me. If Rune had an extra five hundred dollars-plus lying around he wanted to get rid of, he could hand me the cash and I'd put it toward my graduate school debt. I could never say that to Rune, since he thought school was a waste of time. Either way, he would have deducted the cost from my performance pay, so it would have been awash in the end.

"Whatever you say, kiddo," he said in a tight voice, slightly frustrated. We continued on our path to dinner, Louboutin-less.

Beijing Fangshan was no ordinary restaurant. Located in a royal garden surrounded by mountain and water views, the elaborate dining hall was fit for a king. Gold was everywhere. Red-and-yellow dragon and phoenix-themed, it was the epitome of Qing Dynasty luxury. 'Long lasting life' was emblazoned on the silverware and porcelain.

Taking a look around, I was blown away by the surroundings and caliber of people in the room with me. I took a moment to be grateful for my opportunities. It was true that there was no way in hell I would have been able to finagle myself into an event like this without Rune and Click!. But there was no way he could have won over the group without me. I considered us somewhat even at that point.

As the guests mingled about sipping bubbly from champagne flutes, Rune pulled me aside and cold-cocked me.

"You need to make a toast. Now."

My eyes opened wide and heart began pumping blood at three times the normal rate.

"What!?" I asked, hoping I heard him wrong.

"This is the last dinner and your opportunity to take initiative and show leadership in front of a room full of important American and Chinese businessmen," he said in an irritated voice, rolling his eyes and gesturing to the group of suit-clad, white-haired men in the dining hall. "Your *peers.*"

His words were ones of psychological encouragement, but delivered in typical Rune fashion. I stood without speaking, the gears of my brain whizzing.

"That's what you wanted, isn't it?" he asked, incensed at my perceived ungratefulness.

It was true, that's what I wanted. But it was terrifying. In all honesty, I was the person who least belonged in that room. And now I was going to commandeer attention from everyone to deliver an off-the-cuff speech. About what? I would need a minute to think.

"Okay, I—"

"Do it now," he commanded.

It was an ultimatum, with no need to verbalize the alternative.

Fuck, fuck, fuck. What the fuck am I gonna say?

"Okay," I said, swallowing the lump in my throat. Adjusting my dress and hair, I walked back to my seat and picked up my sparkling flute of champagne. Downing it in one gulp, I grabbed another one from a waiter.

You can do this.

Bringing a dainty spoon to the side of my glass and tapping it three times, the room turned to look at me. I froze for a moment.

Holy shit. Man up.

"Excuse me, I'd like to give a toast," I said, melting my fear into a smile. "These past few weeks of the delegation trip have been wonderful. I'd like to thank everyone involved in making this happen, especially the staff who arranged all of the little details that together, I know, can create quite the puzzle. And thank you, Senator, for your dedication to Sino-American relationships, and providing this great opportunity for us to connect with outstanding Chinese businesses," I said confidently, looking him square in the eye. He nodded in approval, happy to be recognized. "I'd like to toast to what I know will be an incredible dinner with new friends. Thank you all for being here." Raising my glass, the group followed in unison.

"Gan bei!" I said joyfully.

They repeated my sentiment and we chugged champagne as the royal dinner commenced. Stuffing our faces with a feast of culinary creations, we devoured regal Qing dynasty delicacies. Swallowtail shark fin, abalone jade toad, oil prawns, and gongmenxianyu, followed by a sampling of famous desserts: pea flour cake, french bean rolls, and sesame cakes with minced pork.

Washing it down with a few more glasses of champagne to celebrate my personal accomplishment, I was thankful Rune forced me to step outside my comfort zone. Throughout the night, delegation members approached me, confessing they wished they had thought of it first. I beamed.

Rune had become increasingly anti-social and irritable toward the end of the delegation trip. Lunch was devoured at Fat Burger after our closing meeting at the Beijing Embassy.

He sat with the group at the table, only to whine about the terrible quality of food everyone was consuming. It was the first American cuisine some people had eaten in days; nobody wanted to hear about the hormones in the meat of their double cheeseburger.

Sandstone was coordinating the lease of a new apartment in Shenzhen. It was a sore subject for days, as it was more expensive than Click! could afford and simply wasn't a plausible option. That type of language doesn't compute with Rune. He reached his breaking point. With no warning, he chucked his Blackberry through the middle of the table's conversation about the global economy and it landed in my fries near a pile of ketchup.

"Don't ruin my phone!" he squawked loudly. Everyone at the table quieted, looking at him with bewilderment. "What?" he continued defensively, "If you do the math, the data on my phone is probably worth fifteen of her lives."

Some of the group gaped at him in astonishment; others ignored him, fed up with his antics. I was stunned at his nerve. Every day.

Turning back to me, "You. You need to wipe that chemical and sugar-filled ketchup off of my Blackberry and handle this menial task without asking me any stupid questions or fucking up like you have been lately." He turned away and began a conversation about importing cheese.

It occurred so frequently those days, but I was in shock that he would speak to me like that, especially in front of other people. Fuck our relationship and politeness, but we both understood saving face. He was doing the opposite: bestowing me as an individual to be respected then tearing me to shreds, valuing me less than a minion. It made us both look like idiots. I was confused. I was angry. I felt stuck.

The delegation was heading back to the States and Rune and I were on our way to Macau. Our goodbyes were especially awkward, considering the uncomfortable scenario the group had just been witness to. Their eyes flooded with sympathy; I knew what they were thinking. The tour bus chugged off down the road as Rune and I slid into the back of a cab in silence. Tension threatened to asphyxiate both of us.

I spoke. "You were really mean to me back there." That was the first time I ever said anything like that to Rune. I never dared to question his treatment of me before. In the beginning he had been harsh but fair. Then it turned into a struggle. Now it was absurd.

He hesitated a few moments before responding in true Rune style, mincing words.

"I was terse."

The blue taxi idled in traffic in front of the Forbidden Palace. I never had the courage to stand up to Rune until now. I had just enough to say it again.

"No, you were fucking mean."

I was defiant. A battle was emerging between my self-respect and this job. When I thought about it that way, fuck Rune and this job. Nothing was worth my self-respect. That's where my courage was coming from.

I realized Rune no longer treated me like a human being. He had no respect for me, pulling out the tar and feathers in front of any willing audience, insulting, degrading, humiliating, and dehumanizing me on a daily basis. And I allowed all of it. *Who was I?* I always valued my self-respect greatly. This wasn't me. *Who had I become?*

Rune tinkered with his Blackberry. "Okay, I was mean," he conceded. "But then you remembered I gave you all my suite upgrades and you weren't upset anymore," he said in an attempt to smooth over the situation.

That just made it worse. His rationalization was the problem. He thought he could use material items or symbols of power to make up for real acts of human decency. Maybe it worked on others, but not for me. In my mind, I screamed and shouted and stomped my feet, yelling, *No, motherfucker, you can't give me a hotel suite then treat me like shit! Fuck you and your stupid hotel suite!*

None of those things mattered to me. In fact, they mattered so little to me that I was overcome with contempt for him because he valued them so much. I didn't know what to say to his juvenile response. He truly was a sociopath who had become supremely obsessed with image, power, and material items, which he erroneously believed could be used to keep me on a leash. I needed some space, to say the least. In real life, I was stuck with him in Asia for another week and a half.

By the time we arrived at the hotel in Macau, I wanted to kill him. I had been dreading the mood of the staff. Click! had serious supply chain issues and there was a mega-crisis at our factory in Tianjin. Spending thousands of dollars and staff time on a weekend retreat didn't sit well with the guys and they all let me know it. I was just looking forward to a break from Rune.

I met Harrison in the first floor cafe at an easy-to-miss table tucked away beneath a staircase. He was masked by thick, chin-length hair, drinking a glass of bloody red wine, wearing jeans and a dark hoodie. His negotiations to join Click! lasted months and he was now officially a team member.

"How are you holding up?" he asked knowingly. Harrison had been acquainted with Rune long enough to understand the frustration from his eccentricities.

I responded without missing a beat. "Rune's lucky I haven't punched him in his fucking face."

He laughed. "I just ignore his bullshit. Best way to deal with it." Shrugging his shoulders, he took a swig of his wine, looking out the window to the sea. "And what the fuck is this Thailand trip? You should tell Rune to fuck off and just go home," he said in all seriousness, pushing his hair behind his ear with his thumb and revealing cryptic eyes that didn't meet mine.

I smiled a real smile for the first time in weeks.

Our conversation was cut short when Rune returned to talk shop with Harrison. I headed up to my room to soak in the tub and decompress.

The evening teetered back and forth between success and disaster, ending with Rune detonating an atomic bomb. I remembered to make dinner reservations this time around, but the restaurant made a mistake, dividing us again into two tables. Harrison, a few photographers and the Chinese speakers were seated together, with myself, Rune, Sandstone, and two brand-newbie China-based Click! employees at another table. Rune was pissed. At me.

Fueling his perpetually smoldering internal fire, Rune was a full-on dictator, pressuring me to eat strange Chinese dishes that even Sandstone wouldn't touch. I was stuck between a rock and a hard place when Rune insisted I eat a Thousand-Year-Old Egg, which is just as it sounds, an egg rotted to perfection. Legend identifies horse urine as the magical ingredient to achieve its ammonia odor. I did my best to deflect the attention, suggesting Sandstone eat it instead.

He tried to pull a fast one. "I'll eat it if Emily eats half," Sandstone said smugly.

"Deal," I replied.

Sandstone's face went white. He never saw it coming. My eyes glinted impishly, happy to have tricked Sandstone but also realizing the joke was on both of us. We split the rubbery blob down the middle. I almost puked all over the white tablecloth.

My favorite BBQ pigeon wings were served next. During the second course, my encounters with Large Larry from Lansing were brought up. I expressed distaste at Larry's sexist behavior and requests for provocative photo shoots. What happened next changed everything.

"You would do a sexy calendar photo shoot for Click!," Rune said matter-of-factly.

Hell motherfucking no, this motherfucker did not just say that shit to me.

My blood ran cold as my temper simultaneously burned hotter than any flame in hell.

Of all the things I knew his crazy ass would do, I didn't ever think Rune would make a remark like that to me. Road dogs for the past year, he was well aware of my need to be respected as a human and never sexually objectified in the workplace.

He was challenging me.

I scoffed indignantly. "No, I wouldn't."

"Yes, you would," he insisted, glancing around the table at the guys, ensuring they take notice of his ability to control my actions. He was drunk on power, eager to display his authority, betting on the fact that I would succumb to him. Not this time. Not about this.

"No, I wouldn't," I said firmly, shooting Sandstone a death stare I knew he understood.

"You would do it if *I* asked you to," Rune pushed.

He pushed too fucking far. No matter how perceptive he thought he was, Rune did not understand my personal convictions. His had eroded to the point that they were all flexible.

"No, I wouldn't. I would quit Click! if anyone seriously asked me to do that. It has nothing to do with my fucking job." My voice was firm.

"You wouldn't quit. You would do it if I asked you to." He would not give up.

"No. I. Wouldn't. Rune." I said, slowly emphasizing every word. Pursing my lips, I swiftly picked up a shrimp dumpling with my chopsticks, jamming it into my mouth before I said something I would regret, saving face for the sake of our guests.

But Rune had crossed the line.

The conversation moved on and I stayed quiet for the remainder of dinner, seething beneath the surface. As soon as the check was paid, I retreated to my suite, stewing in anger. It was the first time I ever seriously thought about leaving Rune and Click!.

The next morning was our company meeting. In the spirit of Christmas a few short weeks away, I brought gifts—hand-stamped, custom leather luggage tags. Everybody loved them. I had one made for Rune and thought it would be petty not to give it to him, despite the circumstances. He acted as if I handed him a hot potato, tossing it carelessly onto the bed.

"Do you like it?" I asked

He shrugged, his face blank. "I don't care about it."
What a dick.

The company meetings didn't go well and were cut short to avoid further embarrassment to Rune. He and I fled to Shenzhen, holing up at the St. Regis for a few days before Thailand. Encouraged by the presence of Harrison, the staff held no punches during the meeting while critiquing Rune's business practices. His ego was badly bruised and he needed to feel important again.

The silent treatment was in effect during our three-hour trek. A year ago it would have hurt my feelings. Now it was welcome alone time. Riding the glass elevator to the lobby of the St. Regis, his instructions to me were curt. I was to obtain the most exclusive suite the luxury hotel had to offer, at a heavily discounted price. Dropping his luggage at my feet he took off down the hallway in typical Rune fashion.

Fluffing my hair and checking my makeup in the mirrored glass, I strutted off in the direction of a reception table manned by a male. With Rune's delicate mental state, I needed to use everything I had to get what I needed to keep him as happy as possible so I could limit my lashings.

I smiled warmly at a Chinese hotel staffer with the chosen English name of Jack, who turned out to be a delight. Not only did he upgrade us to the best two-bedroom suite available, he also recommended Shenzhen Queen's Spa.

Jack obliged my requests to arrange massage appointments for that evening, send someone to unpack Rune's luggage, as well as serve him a hot pot of green tea. I messaged Rune the suite number. No matter what I returned with, I would miss the mark. I knew that.

Rune was impossible to please but I was determined to do what I could to keep him on an even keel. Anything less was counterproductive to my mental health. We were stuck sharing the same air every minute of every day. If he cracked, it would be me and me alone who would be on the receiving end of his breakdown. There would be collateral damage.

Floating on air after two-hour full-body massages, Rune and I ascended to the one hundredth floor of the St. Regis for late-night drinks. Green tea for me and a rare few glasses of red wine for Rune.

"You know, kiddo, the world isn't black and white," he mused, admiring rice fields miles away from 430 meters high. "Sometimes I can't believe where I am now, considering where I started."

I sipped Super Long Jing from a ceramic teacup. Silence was always my friend.

"When I had my first job, my boss told me not to come back without making the sale." He stared into my eyes. "I had no choice. I had to get out my knee pads," he confessed, not wavering.

He meant what he said. His perverse admission didn't surprise me one bit. It was just another day in Rune's achromatic realm.

Rune was erratic, never up or down, left nor right, but all at once. He didn't operate on a schedule regulated by any concept of time. Demanding we work feverishly through the night until the sun shone upon our wall of windows, he would draw the curtains and instruct me to order room service. Hotel staff filled our suite with a lavish display of local cuisine, tea, scones, desserts, and fruits for us to munch on; we laughed and watched stoner comedies on the flat-screen.

I crashed on the couch nestled in the mountain of blankets he set up during our TV marathon. Awakening hours later, crazy Rune was back. Standing over me, eyes wide and cold, he clutched the vest of his favorite three-piece suit from his coveted tailor in Hong Kong.

"Oh, spoiled American princess finally decided to wake up. Good, because there's a hole in my suit!" He waved it around, freaking out. "Get it fixed," he demanded, dropping the vest in my lap and retreating to his bedroom.

I accepted the demeaning behavior and unpleasant words, using all my energy to ward off their negative effect, not allowing his sickness to creep into my sub-consciousness. It would take a simple call to the St. Regis seamstress to fix. Whatever was left of Rune's Zen had most definitely fractured.

Rune and I were hosting an over-the-top dinner party to poach Nigel away from Dumbo. Rune held grudges, biding his time, dead-set on destroying Dumbo little by little even months later. It was an impressive waste of money, even for Rune. It was spectacular though.

The one hundredth floor of the St. Regis was palatial. Three-hundred-sixty views of Shenzhen from the city's tallest building commanded full attention. A spiraling tower of private cubes shrouded in glistening crystals was the center focus. Forking over 5000 RMB for the room alone, I incurred the wrath of Sandstone when he saw the bill come through HQ. He had developed a particular distaste for Rune's uncontrollable hemorrhaging of money.

Still re-inflating his ego, Rune ordered the most expensive bottle of vino on the list. Nigel's girlfriend and her friend discouraged his purchase of a bottle, as they had full drinks already and didn't consume much alcohol. He ignored them, over-pouring three wine glasses then motioning for me to disperse them. They didn't touch the wine.

"You know, that's very expensive wine. The finest money can buy at the St. Regis," Rune said pompously, rudely interrupting their conversation.

The girls looked at each other and giggled uncomfortably, but still didn't drink the wine.

He raged in a silent inferno. There was nothing he hated more than being unable to control someone. Scrambling for a way to save face, he used his best tool. Me.

Breathing fire, he tore into me. "Emily, I don't know why you haven't touched your glass. Click! spent a lot of money on that bottle of wine for you. It needs to be gone by the time we leave. Nigel is driving, and you know I'm a Buddhist. Drink up."

Are you fucking kidding me? Now you're a Buddhist who doesn't drink?

My natural instincts were to lunge across the table and

scratch his eyes out. I loathed him. He made me feel powerless and humiliated. Forcing down glass after glass after glass of incredibly expensive wine, my thoughts were a mélange of good and evil.

Like a sinister architect, darkness shadowed my brain as blueprints were drafted for the perfect international murder. Rune could easily be overpowered using the element of surprise. Water basketball in Macau had proven that.

Alternatively, I could see myself, La Femme Nikita, skulking around the fancy suite after nightfall and slitting Rune's throat while he slept. I was positive Raheem, whom I had kept in touch with from Dumbo, knew someone who would drop the body off in an industrial bone yard for the right price. My loose fingers wavered over a text to Raheem while another guzzle of wine switched me from Dexter-mode to fantasies of soaking up the sun on a beach in Thailand.

In anticipation of the joy found from absolute freedom while exploring a far-off land, I decided Rune would live another day. At least until Koh Samui. It would probably be cheaper to dispose of the evidence there anyway. An hour later I had no thoughts. I was blackout drunk and have no idea what happened past that point.

I suffered from a massive hangover during our travels to Thailand. Cursing the sounds of the world and shielding my eyes from the sun, Rune and I transferred from a train ride to a high-class chauffeured car, then boarded a bus to a far-away airport, from which we flew five hours to Koh Samui, Thailand.

The plane touched down on a narrow black runway of the small Koh Samui airport after dark. It was the first time I exited a plane to a tarmac. The sun had set during our flight and the only lights around were from the tram that transported us to immigration and customs.

It was a noteworthy sight. In America, Germany, China, Macau, and Hong Kong, airports on lockdown 24/7, structured lines, no cell phones allowed, surveillance cameras recording your every move. Koh Samui, was totally different. Everything was open air, with agents perched behind tiki huts, calling you forward to present your identification and papers.

I tripped as I walked toward the customs tiki hut, almost squashing a purplish frog that hopped across my path, heading toward the open field to my right. It was a splendid cultural difference. After collecting our Thailand passport stamps, Rune and I peered out the windows of a cab into the dark jungle during our twenty-minute ride.

The run-down yellow taxi lurched to a stop in front of a group of million-dollar waterfront properties. A local escorted us to our villa by golf cart. Unlocking the exterior wooden gate, we entered a private piece of heaven.

The structure was U-shaped, with an infinity pool sprawled in the middle, and mahogany palapas outfitted with fluffy cushions for napping on either side. Rune's wing sat on the east side of the estate and a short walk across the outdoor patio, my wing to the west.

Although it was late and I was still suffering from the side effects of my hangover, Rune insisted we go to dinner at the swanky villa restaurant. While I washed my hands in the restroom, he ordered me a martini that I was instructed not to waste. I could feel myself wavering on the brink. Alone in Thailand for six more days, there would be no buffer between Rune and I. We would be closer than ever.

We walked along the beach until near sunrise. I slept for a few hours and was back up. Thankfully, Rune was crashing for the day, not to be seen until dinner.

I threw on what would become my uniform for Thailand: a tank top, pink-and-white board shorts, and sandals, and made my way back to the chic restaurant. Relaxing into a chair at a beach side table as I sipped a vanilla latte, I marveled at the rich gem-toned surf.

Why didn't I live here?

I was on the other side of the planet, over twenty-six hours of flight time away from St. Louis. Koh Samui was another world. I knew only one word of their language: *Sawatdee-kah*, which is the way women say hello. A good chunk of my brain had shut down, overworked from the past few weeks, so I abandoned any plans of learning Thai. The Gulf of Thailand was at my feet, weather hot and sunny, culture authentic, and seafood fresh from the stinky ships that morning. I was in paradise.

A small blue taxi dropped me off in downtown Chaweng Beach at a group of cash machines located next to a busy three-way intersection. I grabbed some cash, thousands of Thai currency called Bahts, exchanging at a rate of 30 Baht to 1 USD. I was on a mission to rent one of the scooters Rune had talked so much about. I had zero experience driving scooters, or two-wheeled motorized vehicles in general, but figured it couldn't be that much harder than a bicycle. Crossing the primitive road to the scooter shop proved tedious, dodging reckless drivers.

A petite, no-nonsense, English-speaking Thai lady rented me a Honda scooter for $5 USD per day, filling it with a complimentary dirty vodka bottle full of fuel. She asked if I had driven a scooter before. I told her no.

She proceeded to go around the scooter, instructing me how to turn it on and off, use the blinkers, accelerate, brake, refuel, all the basics were covered. Assuming I received a sufficient tutorial, I signed a form with my name and passport number. She offered me a helmet but I hadn't seen a single person on the island wearing one and shooed it away. I didn't want to stick out like a tourist. I was clearly making poor decisions.

Starting the engine, I checked the mirrors and glanced back at the traffic behind me. I kept reminding myself to drive on the left side of the road. The scooter was in perfect position, so when I was gifted a break in traffic I tweaked the accelerator. It worked, and I entered the correct traffic lane.

A curve was coming up so I turned the handlebars to the left. Nothing happened. I did not turn left. I continued driving straight across the oncoming traffic lane, nearly being smashed by a pickup truck, stopping only when my scooter crashed into a large concrete wall of a convenience store.

Sprawled out on the seething streets of Chaweng, everyone was staring at me. I mean everyone. A few people rushed over to ensure I wasn't seriously injured. Others surveyed from a distance, clearly familiar with dumb tourist accidents. It was awful.

Physically, my right elbow was gushing blood, and pebbles and dirt were ground in my cut up knees. Emotionally, embarrassment was on overdrive. Mentally, I was fucked, stumped by the challenge at hand. The scooter appeared to be unscathed.

I obviously had no idea how to drive a scooter, but it was my only way out of the situation. I had zero Thai linguistic skills, the only person I knew in the country was asleep, and neither of us possessed working cell phones. I was completely alone with no one to save me but me.

Determined to survive, I climbed back on the scooter. People were yelling things at me as they passed. "You're on the wrong side of the road!" The Thai phrases I didn't understand were probably worse sentiments. I ignored them.

Giving myself a pep talk, I restarted the engine, blocking out the local hecklers that had crowded around me. *You can do this. You have to do this. Man up!* My heart beating out of my chest, I accidentally gunned the accelerator, shooting forward into the traffic flow with no warning. Horns blared. I was terrified. Cruising up the hill away from downtown, I realized another left turn was fast approaching. But this time there was no wall on the other side to stop me. A cliff loomed beyond the curve, dropping off into the ocean.

What the fuck. My mind raced. I had no idea what to do.

Although I desperately wanted to turn left, the scooter had a mind of its own, zooming toward the cliff. No solutions came to mind, no forgotten how-to articles on driving mopeds resurfaced, I had nothing. Mentally prepared to die by way of being a stupid tourist driving a scooter directly off of a cliff and into the ocean, I tried turning one last time and instinctively, I leaned. The scooter turned to the left. I had saved my own life. I was shaking uncontrollably, on the verge of tears of terror, and excitement. I couldn't believe it.

Overjoyed to be alive, I concentrated on the rest of the trip back to the villa. I encountered another turn, which I completed in amateur fashion, but at least I stayed on the moped. Spotting the villa ahead on the right, I felt a wave of relief wash over me.

Pulling the scooter onto the gravel near the driveway, I jumped off of it before it stopped moving, falling and scraping my legs once again on the dirty rocks. I didn't care. I was grateful to be alive. Adrenaline coursed through my body, my extremities on pins and needles, heartbeat racing, I felt faint. Chugging my now-warm bottled water, I vowed to never again drive a scooter in Thailand.

This relegated me to riding bitch while Rune drove. It was my only option, as he had officially declared Thai taxis too expensive, and I refused to drive myself. It was awkward.

I had never disliked Rune more than during that week and spent a large part of each day with my arms wrapped around him, my chest pressed to his back. We had literally never been closer. It wasn't a casual, light hold. Being terrified of scooters, I squeezed him for dear life. Every single time I loosened my grip, becoming more comfortable on the scooter and believing that maybe I wouldn't die during the next trip, I would learn a new petrifying fact about scooters in Thailand.

I first read it in our villa welcome book after returning from my near-death experience. Bolded and underlined, tourists were ***not recommended*** to drive scooters in Koh Samui, as it was very dangerous—an estimated over thirty-eight people die per day from scooter accidents in Thailand. Rune scoffed at my apprehension, saying I was a crazy girl for attempting to drive one with no experience, and that he was an expert scooter driver.

"You worry too much," he said, chastising me.

Our vacation was sunshine and rain, and Rune was Dr. Jekyll and Mr. Hyde. Most days he would rise early for high-speed exploring with the scooter. Taking advantage of the time without Rune, I slept late and enjoyed a secret cigarette and peace of mind in the tropical paradise of Thailand alone.

We rode the scooter down the same dirt road to an unassuming open-air tiki hut for breakfast each morning. Set next to a dilapidated, yet still-operating farm, roosters swarmed my ankles, pecking at crumbs beneath the table. Hearty platefuls of succulent shrimp, rice, and veggies cost about $1.25 USD and were accompanied by a free glass of H_2O, although I stuck to my bottled water. There was no way my stomach could handle Thailand's water. The food was fresh and piping hot. I vowed to return to Koh Samui for that meal, if I did nothing else in life.

After breakfast we stopped for our morning massage a bit further down the road. Rune and I were massage obsessed and they were even cheaper in Koh Samui than China. We visited the massage parlors at least twice each day in Thailand, puttering over on the scooter for our mid-afternoon pre-nap massages.

I had my hair braided out of my face and into cornrows while waiting for Rune's massage to end. Misunderstanding the price, I overpaid. Rune found out and went ballistic, listing all my faults that led me to that unforgivable, fucked-up decision making, including my choice of ugly brown shoes, fear of life, and overall decline in performance since Photokina.

Our good days consisted of building sandcastles on the beach, moseying around shaded outdoor markets, and frantically licking three-scoop butter pecan and mint chip waffle cones before the ice cream melted in the eighty-degree weather. Ditching our local spas for the extravagance of Eranda Herbal Spa, Rune and I climbed stepping stones up a beautiful mountainside overlooking the emerald waters of the Gulf of Thailand, disrobing and relaxing under a thatched-roof pagoda, listening to the sounds of cascading waterfalls as two Thai ladies massaged us for over three hours.

An impromptu scooter excursion to the Northeastern corner of Koh Samui led us to the small island of Ko Phan. Menacing alien sculptures made from scrap metal loomed ten feet tall on street corners, only outdone by Ko Phan's Wat Phra Yai, or The Big Buddha Temple. A gold, forty-foot Buddha statue marked the spot, providing me an opportunity for exploration, reflection, and barefoot connection, as shoes were not allowed. Dirty, worn-out flip-flops, bright-colored heels, mud-covered boots, and kid's sneakers sat in a pile at the foot of the temple. No one dared to steal shoes from a worshipper. It was a nice feeling.

That afternoon we joined a well-connected German family living in Hong Kong and vacationing in Thailand for tea on the beach that delightfully turned out to be Moet and fried bananas. Their three-year-old's passport had more stamps than mine ten times over. She was Delta Diamond level status, also received daily massages, and told me quite bluntly that my Chinese wasn't very good.

After our favorite breakfast of shrimp and rice one morning, Rune told me he had a surprise for my twenty-eighth birthday. I had long forgotten what day it was, not looking at a calendar since we left Macau. Forcing me to hold on for dear life unsecured on the back of the death machine, we zipped down the freeway at speeds hovering around 60 miles per hour. Thirty minutes later we arrived at the elaborate gates of a jungle farm set at the foot of a mountain. He idled the moped and I stepped off immediately, shaking the adrenaline out of me.

"Oh my God, I'm so glad we're here. I thought we were gonna fucking die," I said, calming myself and looking around. "What is this place, where are we?"

"Well, you're alive." He did not look pleased by my comments. "You said you wanted to ride elephants, kiddo. Happy birthday," he deadpanned.

"Whoa, for real?" My eyes popped open in excitement. I totally wanted to ride an elephant, especially after I had seen pictures of Tilda doing so in Thailand.

"For real. Enjoy your inhumane activity that abuses animals. I'm not participating. I'm heading out to explore. Don't get captured." He peeled out down the dirt road. I smiled, alone in a jungle in Thailand, about to ride an elephant. What a life.

The elephant ride was an experience. Her name was Emma. Her master Jimi, a Thai local with dark and weathered skin, seated me on the passenger rack but repeatedly asked if I wanted to sit on Emma's rough neck with him. I told him no. He asked about my trip and when he found out I was riding on a scooter, he gasped, horrified.

"You must not ride scooter in Koh Samui! Too dangerous!" He lifted his shirt to reveal his torso, grotesquely deformed and scarred. He had been in an accident while driving a scooter. My scooter-related stress levels once again went through the roof. I frantically tried to calculate the cost of a taxi ride back to the villa in my head.

"You will ride a scooter in Thailand but won't sit on the Emma's neck? Little kids sit on the Emma's neck," he teased me.

That did it. I would not let fear keep me from doing things that little kids do. My chest tight with apprehension, I stepped over the passenger rack and onto Emma's gray, coarse neck, lowering myself into a seated position with Jimi's helping hand. Once I was stable, it wasn't so bad. He took it a step further by jumping to the ground with my phone to take photos, leaving me alone on the elephant.

I freaked out, but Emma didn't run off into the abyss on a rampage or viciously attack me like I imagined. She ambled along happily, sipping water from puddles, playing in the mud, and tickling my feet with her trunk. I relaxed and enjoyed the moment. Roaming around the jungle, through streams, down hills, over fallen trees, I sat upon an elephant, the largest animal in Asia. High above the ground, with a new point of view, I gazed around my surroundings in wonder. My life was surreal at times. I was totally grateful for the experiences allowed me by the universe.

Rune was waiting for me as I said goodbye to Emma and Jimi, promising to visit if I returned to Koh Samui.

"Your animal torture took forever. How was it?" Before

allowing me a chance to respond, he cut in again. "I don't know why you wear eyeliner. You look really low class. Trashy." He cocked his head to the side, scrutinizing me from beyond his nerdy racer-style, reflective-lens sunglasses. "Tilda never wears eyeliner," he said in a condescending tone.

What the fuck. Did he really just say that to me? I stood in silence with my mouth open, dumbfounded.

He flicked his sunglasses over his eyes. "Get on, let's go. We're taking a shortcut because of your irrational fear of scooters on highways," he said, jamming the kickstand with his heel and revving the engine.

Still shocked by the trashy comment, I didn't mention Jimi's full-body deformation from a scooter accident. Moving robotically, I took my place on the scooter, cringing as my arms wrapped around his torso. I was disgusted with the fact that he felt he could speak to me like that. Apparently he could, because I didn't say anything back. I was disgusted with myself.

Our shortcut consisted of driving two hours up the side of a mountain on mostly unpaved terrain, at times completely off-roading, creating our own path. Circling up an incredibly steep paved portion, three street dogs leapt from the trees and began to chase us. Snarling and growling, they caught up quickly, nipping at our heels.

I shrieked in terror, clenching Rune's midsection so tightly that he formed dark purple bruises. Our scooter could only go so fast up the incline, and it wasn't fast enough. A ferocious brown mutt that appeared to be a mixture of pit bull and straight wolf made contact with the back of my flip flop and I screamed bloody murder.

"Motherfuck, Rune! He's got me! Help!! What the fuuuuuck! I'm gonna die!"

I was sure I was going to be pulled off of the scooter, dragged into the jungle and eaten alive by a pack of wild Thai dogs.

Rune sprang into action, expertly balancing the scooter at maximum speed while viciously knocking the savages away with his heel. It wasn't pretty. I shuddered watching Rune's heel crack their jaws repeatedly, but they were trying to kill me. Eventually they dropped back and we sped forward.

"Holy shit! Where the fuck did you learn how to do that?" I asked, gasping for breath.

"Having a deadbeat, junkie, motorcycle-riding father has its benefits," he smiled, wiping beads of sweat from his forehead. At that moment, he seemed almost human. Maybe I was being too hard on him.

I returned his smile and laughed, happy to be alive. Something bad happened and I didn't die. Rune was right all along. We continued plugging away up the path deep into the jungle.

Lush greenery abounded, from the ground beneath our feet to the treetops above our heads. The natural colors of the jungle were vibrant and ethereal. Tiny shacks dotted our sun-soaked path. We detoured for a hike to a majestic waterfall. Removing my shoes, I stood in the trickling stream below it, closing my eyes, saturating in the negative ions flitting around me. It was so calming. Thailand was bliss.

Rune's defiance toward any of my practical suggestions for our exploration route kept us driving in circles on the mountain for hours. Before we knew it, the sun was fading fast and our gas tank was nearly out of fuel with no pump station for miles. The seriousness of our mis-navigation began to set in. Being lost in the jungle of Thailand much longer wouldn't be fun or safe.

Working together as a team, we traversed the jungle with a sense of urgency, expertly avoiding devastating potholes, quicksand, and low-hanging tree branches. As a highway connection appeared in the sunset forty minutes later, we shared a look. Although he would never admit it, I know it was mutual relief.

The excitement of the day left me exhausted and looking forward to my bed. I would not be so lucky, as Rune insisted we spend our last night in Thailand at a ladyboy show. Ladyboys are what Americans would call drag queens. Men dressed as women. What they say about Thailand ladyboys is true: the men often do look better than the women.

I had been to drag shows in the States, but the atmosphere in Koh Samui was very different. Outside the theater, extravagantly made up ladyboys strutted down the sidewalks enticing passers-by, accepting compliments, and posing for photos. Inside the theater were locals, tourists, families with children, couples, friends: you name it. The ladyboys and their lifestyles weren't taboo; they were celebrated and enjoyed by all walks of life.

Our seats were front row and center. Enjoying spiked fresh fruit concoctions, we sang along, laughed and smiled. Rune joined the ladyboys onstage and danced to "Gangnam Style." He made me promise not to show anyone the photos. Then he threatened to fire me if I did, just for good measure.

Strawberry daiquiris on the beach at ArkBar were next on Rune's agenda for my birthday celebration. Lounging with our toes in the sand, local kids roamed around placing exotic animals on people, taking photos of them and then expecting Bahts. I paid for a photo with a lizard on my head before discovering I could have had one with a monkey.

Rune and I talked about life as we sipped tropical frozen drinks, watching fire twirlers ignite putrid gasoline into beautiful hoops of flames while they danced down the coastline, illuminating the night. Rune's mood was semi-amicable, almost relaxed, opening up about his relationship with Tilda after a few drinks.

"We never have sex. I think it's been over a year." He said the words but they weren't attached to anything. "She can be a bitch."

Asking about Saleem, I deliberately kept my feelings close to my chest.

Saleem and I were looming toward a crossroads. Our relationship had surpassed two years, we lived together, and both of us were nearing thirty. I felt pressure to get married. I wasn't elated at the thought of eternal life with Saleem, but I wasn't ecstatic at the thought of life without Saleem either. I wasn't sure how I felt.

We hopped into the bed of a pickup truck decorated like a dragon, our designated driver for the night. Sticking my hands out into the thick, hot air as we rode down the street, Rune snapped on me out of nowhere.

"Why do you insist on dressing like a teenage boy when you're a grown woman? You're so ghetto with your cornrows." He looked at my brown boots in abhorrence. "I hate those fucking shoes. You know I hate those shoes. They're the fucking worst."

I was insulted and surprised that Rune, of all people, would say that. He chose his distinct look, but wanted to dictate my look to suit his preferences, or impress his business connections, or model me after Tilda, or sell his fucking camera bags. I couldn't let it slide.

I pointed to my shoes. "These are my favorite fucking shoes. I bought them in Cologne and have received more compliments on these shoes than any other fucking pair of shoes in my life." Looking at him in his eyes, I said, "I dress the way I do because I like the way I look." I kept going. "Do you just say random fucked-up shit to me just to see when I'll finally stop you?"

Rune was startled yet pleased with my response.

"Yeah, sometimes," he admitted.

"Jesus fucking Christ, Rune." I shook my head. "Cut me a motherfucking break. *Fuck.*"

Neither of us spoke for the rest of the ride, the groans of the pickup truck and sounds of the jungle a welcome distraction.

After our usual tiki-hut breakfast and massage the next morning, Rune and I returned the scooter. Well, that's what we set out to do. The no-nonsense Thai lady was in full effect, asserting that someone had crashed the scooter, demanding $500 USD. Although Rune knew that I had crashed the scooter into a wall once and I was positive he had wiped out more than a few times, Rune threw a tantrum, stomping around and shouting.

Ripping the keys from the Thai lady's hands, he ordered me back on the bike. I did what I was told. We tore off up the road to a lot filled with hundreds of scooters. He promptly parked the scooter and left the keys in the ignition. Then he flagged a taxi and we headed to the Koh Samui airport. That scooter was in my name; he didn't care.

We arrived in Hong Kong late in the evening and stopped for steamed dumplings at Jade Restaurant in the airport. It was Rune's favorite and had become mine too. Hundreds of people stormed around the terminal as we sipped our green tea, carefully soaking our dumplings in little white trays of soy sauce.

"I just booked a one bedroom suite with a desk in the living room. You know, to save money since you spent it all on your hair," Rune said snottily. I would never live down the cost of braiding my hair. "Your flight leaves early and you have a lot of work to do so you can use the office to pull an all-nighter and I'll sleep in the bedroom." He popped a dumpling into his mouth. I had nothing to say.

After a midnight stop to a Hong Kong massage parlor, we took the subway to the hotel. Beneath the light of the desk lamp, I accomplished a fair amount of work, leaving around 4:30 am to catch the subway to the airport.

In an act of friendship and thoughtfulness, Rune awoke to gift me cold dumplings for carry-on food and wish me safe travels and happy holidays. I tossed them in the trash at the airport, not wanting to accept any more favors from him, no matter how small or insignificant.

6 MAN VS. SELF

The beginning of 2013 was gleefully devoid of Rune and Tilda, who were vacationing together in Asia for a couple of weeks. Sandstone and I resumed our roles in St. Louis, happy to be reunited, although times had changed and we didn't need one another as much anymore.

Using the down time to contemplate my career, there was no question that a parallel move would be unsatisfying. My next position had to be the right come up. It would take time.

A weekend trip in Las Vegas to attend a trade show with Harrison was on the work agenda. This would be our first chance to really get to know each other. I was looking forward to it.

I had never been to Vegas but Harrison was a vet. We started our night in the bar of the hotel. Harrison was clad in jeans, a dark hoodie, and my favorite pair of his shoes—gray suede boots like Reid's. Chin-length light-brown hair tucked behind his ear, Harrison's frame was tall and lean, as a cyclist and runner. I once joked about his shirt size being a sMedium. I'm pretty sure he didn't like that.

Harrison greeted me with an eyebrow raise. "What's up?"

I was immediately at ease. We ordered drinks and commenced the obligatory bitching about Rune, bonding over the craziness and nonsense. He vocalized the fact that I was smarter than my job and we both agreed that if I stayed at Click!, Rune would never let me advance. I would be his one and only forever, and nothing else. Harrison encouraged me to seek better opportunities. I listened.

Our conversation moved to personal lives, discussing stories about our college experiences, favorite musicians, and traveling the world. We shared a love of hip-hop and people watching, and were both afflicted with an overall predisposition to counter-culture and migraines.

Harrison was super intelligent, creative, successful, wealthy, well connected, and remarkably down-to-earth. Profanity littered his speech, similar to the sailor's mouth I often channeled. As a blonde-haired white kid raised in pre-gentrified Brooklyn, New York, Harrison—like me—understood the dualities of life experiences. Although he had always been well heeled, he wasn't oblivious to the gamut of life. Far from it.

After toasting to the Beastie Boys and knocking back a few more drinks, he took me on a walking tour of Vegas. We hit all the major spots for people watching. Hysterics accompanied us for hours, our fucked-up humor finding kindred spirits in one another.

Unconventional, unabashed, unapologetically himself is what he was at all times. He didn't give a fuck what anybody thought of him. I was in full-on power-attraction mode when I discovered this air he had about him. It wasn't only my opinion. Everybody in the office had a sort of man-crush on Harrison, including Sandstone, Reid, and Remy. His dark features and detached attitude gave him a strung-out, heroin-chic-esque appearance and innately cooler-than-you vibe. It was hot as hell.

Harrison and I walked a good distance to and from the show each morning and night, preferring the sunshine and fresh air to stuffy recycled A/C while waiting in long cab lines indoors. Trekking back to the hotel the last evening of the show, we agreed to meet in the bar in thirty minutes. It was Harrison's fortieth birthday and there was fun to be had.

The bartender refilled our drinks after a round of shots, and we analyzed a map of Harold & Kumar's route to White Castle, drawn on a napkin by Harrison to prove a point. On our third refill, the bartender informed us that mud wrestling would soon be taking place nearby. Harrison snorted in amusement.

Shortly thereafter, we found ourselves straddling horse-saddle bar stools, surrounded by men hooting and hollering around an inflatable wrestling ring filled with chocolate pudding. The cover was astronomically pricey for the lowbrow talent that awaited us inside so I worked my magic on the doorman, scoring free entrance for both Harrison and I. He thanked me with a shot.

"Are you ready for this?" he yelled over the music, glancing toward the stage with trepidation.

"Hell yeah!" I responded, extending my glass to cheers.

We laughed and drank while the girls sloshed around in the pudding. Our running commentary kept me in stitches. After a surprise blonde giant in a pink bikini was unleashed to squash the unsuspecting nightly participants, we picked up new drinks and settled into a row of slot machines near the elevators, Harrison's favorite spot for late-night Vegas people watching. We were not disappointed with the selection of passersby.

The next morning we met for breakfast and shared a taxi to the airport. I had an awesome time and felt like Harrison had become a friend. Staring through the thick oval window during takeoff, Sin City became smaller and smaller. I would be in St. Louis soon, back to reality, back to my dilemma with Saleem.

All mixed up, a pit of dread gnawed at my gut. I didn't want to hurt Saleem or break my commitment. But I also wanted to be happy.

There had been casual mention of a ten-year commitment ceremony for Rune and Tilda on some exotic island. However, as I had learned to do with so many other whimsical sentiments that came out of Rune's mouth, I ignored this idea. If acknowledged, it became real.

I had so much other work to do for the development of the

actual company I had no time for their bullshit and wanted no part of it. Deep down, part of me knew at some point and time my sociopathic boss would insist that I join the ceremony planning. I kept my distance as long as I could.

The moment I stepped foot into the office after Vegas, I was ushered into a meeting and informed that I had been the lucky person chosen to be Rune and Tilda's 'fixer' for their wedding in the Republic of Panama. The commitment ceremony had turned into a full-blown wedding, complete with a white dress, rings, cake, and legal paperwork.

I was tasked with planning the wedding and reception, organizing the entire trip for thirty-plus guests of varying ages and travel experience, and attending the ten-day event as a personal slave for each individual. As usual, this would all be in addition to my normal work duties. And I would make it happen in one month.

"It's super easy," Rune said. "It will be a vacation."

I knew it was a train wreck waiting to happen.

Everyone asks me why I didn't say no. The reality of the situation is that this person signed my paychecks. He would be quick to tell any stranger on the street that my performance pay was completely arbitrary and entirely at his discretion. The next question was, inevitably, "Why didn't you just quit?"

I needed money. I was essentially supporting two people: myself and Saleem. Working as a social worker and then for local government before Click!, while also paying for graduate school out of pocket, I was not a rich individual. I had never suddenly quit a job without having another one lined up.

My life had always been very structured, very safe. With a sociopath for a boss, saying no brings the possibility of jeopardizing that safety in an instant. I had put up with so much over the past year, hell, over the month of December alone. I had already started talking with associates about new opportunities, with hopeful plans to move on within the near future.

I thought to myself, *What's one more trip?*

Forcing a smile, I yielded. "Okay."

Immediately regretting my decision, I was expected to create the perfect wedding for the most pretentious, cheap, and just plain unreasonable couple in the entire universe. Never mind the fact that I had zero experience with nuptials, had never been to Panama, and barely spoke Spanish. None of those things mattered to Rune and Tilda. With those two, I was fucked from the get-go.

I hit roadblocks at every turn of the planning stage. By stroke of luck, a connection I made a few months prior happened to know a guy in Panama. That's how I met Gary, a Canadian from Saskatchewan living in Panama City.

Even with his local knowledge and connections, arranging a wedding on such a short time frame was incredibly stressful. Rune and Tilda were no average bride- and groom-zillas. And I was the furthest thing from a wedding planner.

Saleem and I jetted off on a week-long Mexican vacation right before the Panama wedding shenanigans began. Planned a year prior, it would be Saleem's first time leaving the country. As our flight departed, he jammed out to reggae music in his headphones while I brooded over the state of our relationship. My satisfaction and fulfillment had steadily deteriorated over the past year. I didn't want to admit it, but it had become too much to ignore.

When I was in China for the first time, we spoke on the phone once—maybe twice—during my three-week trip overseas. Email was sparse—I convinced myself it was because he would never check it anyway.

Our communication was no different during Photokina. Time spent with Gabe in Cologne was nothing more than that, but it was fun. Emailing Saleem a photo of a Chinese poker club the second day of the delegation trip, he wouldn't cross my mind again until Rune asked about him weeks later on the beach in Thailand.

Time at home was so boring. My psyche would never be the same after my experiences, my perspective permanently altered. Life couldn't go on as it had before. I was intrigued by endless possibilities, my mind working its way through evolution.

Saleem stayed the same. Maybe we were just stuck in a rut. I looked to our time in Mexico as the crystal ball. The trip would tell me everything I needed to know.

I drove our rental sedan over a minefield of potholes on the semi-paved road thirty-ish minutes from the airport to downtown Cabo San Lucas. Saleem wasn't much help navigating the short, sparsely signed, one-way streets of Cabo, but was effective in getting us more lost. I finally seized the map from him and figured it out myself.

We had a perfectly fine time in Cabo, sightseeing whale skeletons in Plaza Amelia Wilkes and frolicking around the white sand beaches and cerulean water at Playa del Amor. Filling our bellies with fresh shrimp omelets and sugarcoated fruit empanadas before massages and fruity umbrella drinks on the beach, we couldn't have painted a better scene.

Speeding up Mexico 19 along the pristine coast to Playa Cerritos, we danced to salsa music in the car while drinking frosty cervezas, the wind blowing hair into my eyes. Mornings were spent in surfing class, clad in wet suits bobbing on waxed boards over the sparkling water. I picked up the basics quickly but destroyed my toes in the process. Our classmates were a friendly couple we paired up with for zesty fish tacos prepared from the day's catch and heavily-poured salty margaritas in Todos Santos, a primeval art town with a rapidly developing film and music scene.

Saleem and I had ample room in an enormous four-poster bed with dungeon balcony doors open and welcoming the serene sounds of Baja California Sur. Our secluded Hacienda was over-the-top romantic, positioned at the edge of the North Pacific Ocean. Breading fish for dinner together in the colorfully tiled Mexican kitchen, a mini flour fight broke out, ending in laughter and a mess. On our last evening, we enjoyed Chef Saleem's cuisine and my attempt at flan while relaxing on the terrace watching the sunset. The sky was a time-lapse watercolor painting in vivid hues of raspberry sorbet and peaches and cream. Everything was perfect.

It all meant nothing to me. I looked at him and felt apathy. Maybe things were different at one time, but there was nothing left anymore. I couldn't have been more bored with my companion and there was no denying it any longer. Our relationship had run its course.

I decided to keep my feelings to myself for the moment. There was no time. I was scheduled to leave for Rune's wedding in Panama less than forty-eight hours after Saleem and I returned to St. Louis. This would all have to wait until I came back from Central America with a clearer head.

7 PANAMOCALYPSE

Rune and Tilda's ten-day wedding celebration would begin in Panama City and continue to the archipelago of Bocas del Toro and Bastimentos Island for a week. Elizabeth and I met at the airport in St. Louis. Rune begged me to accompany her to Panama. Britton, Rune's best friend and boyfriend of Elizabeth, couldn't make it due to work obligations but Elizabeth was attending as wedding photographer and guest of the groom.

We landed at the Panama Tocumen Airport and I located the scattered wedding guests, herding them toward the passenger pick-up area. Then the trouble began.

As impossible as it would seem, it appeared that other people like Rune and Tilda existed in the world. Approximately thirty. And they were all on this trip.

The guests complained about the "overwhelming" heat, "unbearable" weight of their suitcases, "difficult-to-understand" interaction with immigration, and "inconvenient" delay for van pick-up. My stress levels rose and I braced myself for the wicked week ahead.

The van pulled up eighteen minutes late, a not-so-helpful guest pointed out. The drive only took twenty minutes, with unusually light Panama City traffic. The guests bitched about the transit time. My suspicions of a wicked week had now increased to the possibility of vicious.

Rune and Tilda were hanging out in the lobby of the hotel. I assessed Rune's mental state as he shoved an ice-cold screwdriver in my hand, ordering me to relax. He was in uber-host mode and no matter how tired I was or how much I didn't want to stay up drinking all night, that's what I would be doing.

I'd spent enough time with him to identify which of his personalities he was displaying and adapt my demeanor to match. I didn't do this for fun. Those unfortunate enough to work with Rune know it as self-preservation.

I met the rest of Tilda's family, her siblings and their significant others, aunts and uncles, cousins and nieces, grandparents and friends. With the exception of Rune's three family members and friend Nicky, everyone was cold and distant. Keenly aware of the vile atmosphere surrounding Tilda's family, their suppressed emotions of revulsion and impatience were transparently obvious behind their Stepford Wife-like interactions with me, the Help.

I snuck outside to meet Gary. After hours of work on his behalf, Rune and Tilda insisted that I not compensate him, arbitrarily deciding he contributed nothing of value. I was appalled but not surprised. This was normal Rune and Tilda behavior. They do not value people.

In reality, Gary was the core component to the entire event. He provided us with local networks as our eyes and ears on the ground. Most importantly, Gary successfully negotiated our thirty-plus-person deal for Air Panama flights, no easy feat. Bags of cash and passports are the only way to get it done.

Despite Rune and Tilda's explicit instructions not to, an envelope full of cash was exchanged and he was on his way.

It was only $500 USD; they would never even notice. At any given time, my backpack contained around $7,000 USD to be used at my discretion, which happened to trump Rune's at the moment. We had an agreement with Gary, he fulfilled it, and I paid him. That's how life should work.

Slipping back into the lobby, I mingled with guests long

enough for Rune's liking, retiring to my room at about 1:30 am. I was dead tired.

Nine more days. I sprawled across the queen bed, audibly sighing at the thought of what was to come. Closing my eyes, I never would have guessed that would be one of the last nights I would have the privacy of a bed to myself. After all those months, days, hours, minutes, and seconds with Rune, I should have known better. I was so naïve.

Rune and I were flying to Bocas del Toro the next morning while the rest of the guests toured the Panama Canal, to arrive in Bocas later that evening. This would be my only pre-chaos peace for the next ten days. I just had to get the group from the hotel onto the bus.

Humidity engulfed me as I walked out of the lobby onto the busy streets of Panama City, frizzing my hair as soon as my foot hit pavement. I performed a head count once the cattle were buckled up on the minibus, fielding requests for mixed drinks, hairspray, solar chargers, an oral history of the Panama Canal, and weather updates for Bastimentos Island. Magic Emily took over and efficiently denied, fulfilled, or ignored the requests, escaping the bus before it departed.

Rune and I jumped in a cab.

"We get a little break from Tilda's family, huh?" he said, laughing.

I didn't know if I was allowed to laugh at Tilda's ridiculous family or not. Exhaling, my body slouched back into slight relaxation. I had to stay on my toes or Rune was liable to give me a heart attack.

Arriving at Albrook Marcos A. Gelabert International Airport, Rune shoved his passport into my hands and brusquely walked away. Rune liked to pretend he was extremely important, refusing to do anything himself that could be done by a minion. He often emailed me while standing at the ticket counter at the airport, instructing me to call Delta and change his flight or finagle a free seat upgrade to business class.

Checking into our Air Panama flights to Bocas del Toro was the worst. It didn't help that I also had to make changes to the group's afternoon flight and Tilda added guests to the list after all of the seats were sold out. This mattered little to her, insisting they travel together on one flight no matter what.

The flight changes would involve bumping ticketed passengers from their seats and replacing them with our guests. A little bribery was in order. This was a complete non-issue in the shade of gray Rune and I lived in.

I had already given in to my slave status, forsaking a shower that morning and applying only a light coat of mascara for makeup, to ward off "you look tired" comments. My outfit consisted of dark fitted jeans, a red Bob Marley T-shirt, green fleece picked up in Cologne, and seven-dollar white-and-green tennis shoes purchased with the express intent of being destroyed in Panama.

I was sweating. I didn't look very cute, definitely not ideal for influencing someone with my feminine guiles. In the end, my eyes and smile (and stacks of cash) won out, and I got what I wanted. The group would fly together; crisis averted.

Rune and I boarded a tiny fifty-passenger plane after a thirty-minute delay. Buckling my seat belt, I closed my eyes and reclined to relax.

"Let's talk shop," he interrupted my quiet time.

Defeated, I moved my seat to the upright position.

"We need to discuss our new hires, drama with Luca, my plans to direct ten non-Click! related commercials in 2013, our new Chinese factory relationship, boosting our social media presence, sending Remy back to China, and preparing for photo shows in Beijing, Australia, and the South of France. You'll be attending and running all of those events."

I listened and played along, nodding and verbally affirming at the correct times. Throwing in an expertly placed laugh and scoff with an ambiguous statement when he griped about the staff was my exit route that satisfied both parties. He received his confirmation bias, ignorant to the fact that I was being less than sincere. I stayed within his good graces and managed to deflect his ruthlessness away from my hard-working colleagues.

I had become The Gatekeeper of Rune. I wasn't the only way to him, as he was the talented Mr. Ripley, a constantly networking subhuman being encountering people from all walks of life every day. Despite his horrid treatment of me, I was still the favorite. Sacrificing my iron exterior to the fire upon arrival over a year ago, he beat me into a likeness of his own image.

Rune considered me his loyal right-hand man, closest friend, and maybe even family. If I had an opinion, he gave it adequate consideration. I could keep people out, or bring people in. There were times I kept people out due to retribution from Rune, as well as times I kept people out for fear of tangling them in Rune's fucked-up world. He would always burn them. No one was exempt.

Our minuscule plane hit jarring turbulence. The flight crew informed us there was a problem with the engine. A voice from the cockpit crackled over the intercom, in Spanish first, then English.

"Prepare for an emergency landing."

Fuck. Tightening my seat belt, I thought about my family, my talents, my dreams, and my reality.

What the fuck am I doing on this plane with Rune?

Assessing the past year of my life in hyper speed, I realized that if I died at that moment, I could not say I was truly happy. Yes, I was flying around the world to exotic lands often basked in luxury that most people couldn't imagine even in their wildest dreams. I worked for an exciting company alongside some of the most inspiring people in the world. I was always learning, doing, and accomplishing, my career and mind stimulated. But I wasn't happy.

The quality of my life was diminished because my days were spent hanging out with a sociopath. Eroding my self-esteem and happiness, no hotel suite, elephant ride, cold dumplings, or fake vacation to Panama could change that. I spent more than 9,000 hours of my life as Rune's slave, jumping at his every beck and call. I needed to figure out my exit route, and soon.

The landing was less than smooth but we were safe on the ground. The crew tinkered with the plane for an hour before assuring us everything was fine. We had to take their word.

Arriving in Bocas del Toro hours behind schedule, I still had to check-in, collect keys, walk-through all the villas with a list provided by Tilda to "ensure the staff doesn't cut corners," then perform any follow-up cleaning required to meet her written standards.

Before leaving St. Louis, Tilda lectured me on her preferred manner of cleaning floors or lamps or whatever she imagined I'd be scrubbing.

"Don't break your back cleaning. Your best effort is fine. But don't be lazy," she ended nonchalantly.

After that, I had to retrieve golf carts from the dock and drop them off at the villas, find and charge eight Panama cell phones, program helpful numbers into said phones, locate an open store to purchase ten bottles of shampoo and conditioner, and pick up thirty guests at the airport, escorting them back to the Island. No sweat. Just another leisurely day in Rune's labyrinth.

Brainstorming ways to kill two birds with one stone, I tapped my foot impatiently as we stood next to the baggage claim at the Bocas del Toro airport. I wouldn't have checked any luggage but Rune and I were both dragging around a shitload of 'necessities' Tilda insisted we bring.

It was overcast when we exited the airport onto the streets of Bocas. Walking through town to catch a water taxi over to Bastimentos Island, I surveyed the area, sweeping my gaze from side to side, taking in the subtleties of my new surroundings.

Beneath our feet were cracked and missing sidewalks, mud seeping through ruts in the road. Happy shacks of rainbow palettes lined the streets, providing a symbolic contrast to the dingy, stained working-class wardrobes hanging from clotheslines in the hot sun. An old fruit stand leaned on the corner. Their offerings were fresh: thick yellow bananas that could pass as wiffle bats, bright green guanabanas, and brown hairy coconuts bearing honeyed milk. Stray dogs chilled in the streets, soaking up heat and panting to stay cool. A certain pace was set in Bocas and it wasn't rushed.

I paid close attention to our route. The next few days would bring me back this way again and I needed to be an expert to navigate alone. Statues, buildings, street names, and historical landmarks were etched into my brain as points of reference in order for me to fast track my familiarity. Thirty people were about to turn to me for directions and leadership. I could show no weakness or the mob would eat me alive.

We caught a water taxi across the Caribbean Sea with Rune paying the fee, $5 USD per person. Tilda forbade me to ever pay more. Our third-world water taxi was old and rickety with a shallow pool of water floating in the bottom. The paint was peeling and there were no cushions on the weathered wooden planks that served as seats.

Sparkling blue water surrounded our small craft as we zoomed out into the jewel ocean. Passing tropical islands brimming with greenery, the temperature a balmy eighty degrees Fahrenheit, it was nirvana indeed.

Our driver informed us a storm was coming through. Wind speeds increased and the waves were unforgiving. Large swells caused me to fly off of the bench, bruising my butt on the way back down. It was not a very enjoyable ride and would be the first of many.

Puttering slowly through the no-wake zone, Bastimentos Island appeared in front of us. Docking away from the straw-colored beaches in a shaded opening to the plant-covered living rainforest, we walked the creaky wooden plank surrounded by a shaded jungle enclave to the reception desk.

I would perform the check-in drill, clipping a hefty string of keys to my belt loops, a bag full of cell phones in my left hand, and jingling the keys to golf carts in my right. Check-in went much more smoothly than I anticipated. Central America seemed to have their shit together on a different level than Asia.

Reception warned me about a large vat of clay that had been spilled on the road by construction workers. Unable to clear the muck, the only option was to wait for it to dry out when the rain stopped for a few days. This would never happen.

The golf cart sluggishly plowed through the quagmire up the hill as I drove Miss Daisy to his villa. Rune pranced around like Michael Alig in his heyday, admiring and criticizing everything at the same time. I set off to complete my tasks, arranging a villa staff member to drop off the golf carts and checking off each box for the villas within record time.

The sun would soon set. Tilda and company were to arrive in Bocas in forty minutes. That gave me just enough time to get to town and do my shopping on the way to the airport. Grabbing my backpack, I threw on my dollar-store sunglasses I was sure to lose and headed down to the dock.

Hopping in an almost full water taxi, I sat down and a techno ringtone blared from my backpack. There were eight Panama phones on me at the time. I had no idea which one was ringing. Frantically pulling cell phones out of my bag, I inspected them one-by-one. The weather was getting worse and the boat was rocking, making it difficult for me to balance everything.

It was Rune, calling to tell me that the villa floors were not cleaned to his satisfaction. I was to rectify this before Tilda and the group arrived. This was not logically possible.

I was onboard a water taxi in the middle of the sea, facing an impending storm. The staff at the resort had gone home for the evening, so there was nobody to delegate. I didn't exactly have a bunch of free time between the boat ride and shepherding the helpless rich idiots back to the island. There was no way I could magically re-clean the villa floors while simultaneously picking up everyone at the airport.

That would be no simple task either. Transporting thirty people around a third world island town aboard water taxis across the Caribbean Sea and through the rainforest on golf carts required the full-time attention of at least three people, but there was only me. Every single thing Rune asked of me was incredibly difficult if not completely impossible.

"What's that all about?" someone chortled in the background. I snapped to attention and turned around. Behind me sat a couple, a short-haired blonde lady next to a man with a bald head reflecting the sun. Both wore relaxed smiles.

"Hi." I flashed a smile and began to reorganize the items in my backpack. "I'm here for my boss's wedding. It's at Playa Bluff. I'm their *fixer*," I emphasized with air quotations.

"Oh really?" they said. "Do you live here?"

"Yes, really. And no, I've actually never been to Panama before." I replied almost robotically as I continued about my business, responding to emails and writing to-do lists. It was only the second day and this conversation kept repeating itself when people discovered my purpose in Panama. I knew what was coming next so I got to it first.

"And no, I don't speak Spanish."

"Wow!" they said, firing off more questions. "How long are you here? How many people are in the group? How is that working out for you?"

An email came through about that evening's barbecue dinner. With my gaze zoned in on my phone, I rattled off matter-of-factly, "The trip is ten days. I'm on day two. There's thirty people. It's terrible. They're all stuck-up entitled assholes, and my boss's wife is a cunt." They laughed out of shock and amusement.

I typed a reply as I continued. "I don't even really do this. I'm not a wedding planner. My boss just asked me to come on this trip as a favor to him. He said it would be a vacation, but I knew it wouldn't. I said yes, but totally realize I should have said no. They treat me like I'm their slave."

"What does your company do?" the person sitting next to me asked.

"I work for Click!, a company that sells camera packs for adventure photographers; people who hang off of helicopters and climb mountains to get their shots." Pressing send, I tucked the phone in my bag, zipping and fastening it to my back. "It's a really cool company. My boss is just crazy and his wife is worse."

I looked up at my seatmate who was looking at me, suddenly noticing he was not unattractive. Wearing a black T-shirt and swim trunks, a pile of thick dark hair sat atop his head. Smiling broadly, he revealed a row of perfectly straight blizzard-white teeth framed by a hawkish nose and concrete jawline. Day-old scruff covered the lower half of his face. His stately grin caused me to smile back without realizing. The wind blew his shirt up ever-so-slightly to where I caught a glimpse of his tanned abs. He was fit. Black shades covered his eyes.

A magnetic force drew me to him, an invisible Kevlar thread suddenly connecting the two of us. It was strong. I felt it in my chest. The universe pushed us together on that water taxi on purpose. I didn't know why yet.

"Never heard of Click!. Are they like Lowepro?" he asked.

"Yeah, that's one of our main competitors. Are you a photographer?"

"He is now," said the guy from the back of the boat.

The man next to me smiled.

They were from Australia, on a customer appreciation trip with the man next to me who, they explained, owned a plumbing supply store. The conversation was lively and a nice break from Rune and Tilda's bullshit. By the time the water taxi docked in Bocas, it was discovered that we would all be in Panama City that upcoming weekend. Exiting the boat, I unzipped my backpack to grab payment for the driver.

"Shit. I only have fifties and hundreds. Do you guys have any change?" I pleaded with the Aussies as we swayed on the dock. Panama's currency was the Balboa, but everyone used USD, as they exchanged at an equal rate.

"I'll take care of it," said the man who sat next to me on the boat.

"Thanks so much, I appreciate it. I'll have to come find you guys after I get change to pay you back," I said.

"Don't worry about it. Just meet us in Panama City this

weekend for a drink," he said as he paid the taxi driver for my fare.

I responded without premeditation, "Deal."

The couple from the boat scampered into their Bocas hotel. The man and I were alone on the dock. Steel gray clouds now covered the sky, jolts of lightning above us flashing warnings of rain. We retreated to a deserted tiki bar between the hotel and dock, the patrons choosing to drink inside until the sun returned.

Removing our sunglasses, our eyes met, instantaneously igniting a spark that surged throughout our bodies from head through heart to pinky toe and back. The world paused for ten lifetimes. Staring into each other's eyes, we were shrouded in a strange veil of intimacy. I couldn't look away.

Without breaking our electric gaze, he spoke confidently, "I'll give you my number so we can meet up."

Indescribably caught up in his essence, I agreed immediately.

"Okay." My voice was hypnotic.

"My name is Dmitri," he introduced himself as I saved his number in my phone.

"I'm Emily," I responded with a dopey smile.

Tangled in the intoxicating energy between the two of us, we were unable to tear our toffee eyes from each other. An unknown force held us beneath the empty tiki hut where we were supposed to be, life existing only in slow motion breaths of dharma.

After a few minutes gravity pulled me back to earth and I shook my head, blushing. I had to get going. The guests would soon arrive. We said our goodbyes sharing a pensive look, oddly reluctant to part ways with a stranger, but destined to meet again in Panama City.

Checking the time, my trip to outer space with Dmitri had cost me the fifteen minutes I set aside for shopping. *Shit.* I stepped onto the streets of Bocas, memories from the earlier trip my guide to the airport. Fat droplets of rain splattered across my face. I had no umbrella. Things looked different in the dark.

Five minutes later, I received a call from Rune saying that the group's flight was canceled due to dangerous weather. I would need to rebook them. *Fuck*. Not two minutes later, Tilda called on another cell phone. Asking Rune to hold on, I struggled to search through the phones to answer her call. Standing in the middle of a dirt road in the pouring rain juggling eight cell phones, I spotted a table with an umbrella and decided it would be a good idea to chill for a minute and figure out my next move. Two guys sat underneath. While holding two conversations on two separate cell phones, I asked them, "Can I sit down for a sec?"

They were intrigued with whatever the hell I had going on and ushered me into a seat. I managed to finish my conversation with Rune, who added a dozen more items to my shampoo run. Tilda barked orders for an airport pick-up, hotel accommodations, dinner reservations at a restaurant that could comply with her crazy dietary restrictions, and an activity for after dinner.

I took care of Tilda's immediate needs, arranging for a ride from the airport to a recommended hotel with a low negotiated rate that included breakfast and Wi-Fi, ensuring they had a guide to escort them to wonderful local cuisine in Panama City that evening, with an optional moonlit tour of the Amador Causeway. I did it all within ten minutes from a burner pay-as-you-go Panama phone, outside in the pouring rain, speaking English only, with no prior Panama City expertise.

Of course, Tilda was not impressed by my choice of hotel, room rate, or restaurant. Their driver was ten minutes late, and she was "not happy" that I had recommended such an unpopular activity, as none of her guests chose to participate in the moonlit walk.

Introducing myself to the guys at the table, Tom and Corey were from California. Once they heard a snippet of my story, they fixed me a few strong drinks. I ended up spending two hours under their umbrella talking about life.

After three drinks we came to the conclusion that the

weather was just going to get worse. The guys gave me directions to a convenience store where I could purchase shampoo and wished me luck.

Once my backpack was filled to the brim with shampoo and other frivolities, I was back out on the dark streets in the pouring rain. Walking around Bocas wasn't that bad, even soaking wet head-to-toe, but now the storm was setting in with strong, cold winds and deep rumbling thunder. It was time to get back to Bastimentos Island. I had been ignoring Rune's calls for at least three hours at that point.

The water taxi companies were closed. I entered the lobby of a waterfront hotel asking for help, wiping my soaked feet on the welcome rug as best I could. The desk attendant, Kas, explained that due to the weather and fact that it was 10:00 pm, it would be difficult to find a boat.

She chatted on the phone in Spanish for a good ten minutes and informed me that a driver agreed to take the challenge of ferrying me over to Bastimentos in the storm. However, the ride that normally cost $5 USD was now $50 USD. Fifty-dollar boat rides were definitely not in Tilda's budget, but I didn't care.

Thanking Kas profusely, she graciously waved me off. From Dmitri covering my taxi fare, Tom and Corey providing drinks and shelter from the rain, Kas arranging my ride, and the driver who agreed to fight the storm to take me to the island, strangers had really helped me out that day.

I thought about what traveling had shown me. It was good to be open to new people, places, and things. *Everything wasn't so scary*.

I stepped into the storm. The hotel had a few lights but they didn't reach far. I could barely see. Rain pelted my face and body at a rate that made it futile for me to attempt to keep dry at all. Walking to the edge of the wobbly dock, balancing carefully in order not to fall off, I took in the churning Caribbean Sea.

In the distance, I could faintly hear the persistent chugging of a boat. My eyes adjusted to the darkness as it appeared in front of me, water loudly slapping the wooden sides. It was a tiny fishing boat with no awning to shield from the rain, no lights to navigate in the dark, and no life preservers in case of emergency.

"Hola!" I greeted the man who was kind or stupid enough to escort me.

"Hola," he grunted.

"Bastimentos?" I asked, hoping I was getting on the right boat. Kas had only spoken to him on the phone, unable to give me a description. I had no idea what he looked like. For all I knew, I could have been getting into any stranger's boat. It was dark, late, stormy, and I was the only living soul on the dock other than that man who came puttering up.

"Si," he answered, while fiddling with the gas tank.

"How much?" I played dumb, my last attempt at negotiation.

"Late, bad weather, dangerous. Fifty," he said definitively.

Looking out into the murky abyss, I thought about the possible outcomes of this situation, many of which were negative. I was concerned but had no choice. Tightening the sternum strap on my backpack, I nodded.

"Okay," I agreed.

He extended his hand and guided me into the boat. I sat rigidly on the only row of seating and put on my sunglasses in an attempt to shield me from the rain and wind. Grasping the sides of the boat and planting my feet firmly on the ground for stabilization, I ducked my head and braced myself for less-than-smooth sailing.

The voyage proved to be far more terrifying than I imagined. The storm was vicious, loud thunder cracking and lightning flashing in the sky. The massive white-capped waves poured over the sides of the boat, filling it with water. Battering us around on the angry sea, I could never tell when they were coming until the wet foam hit me in the face. Without lights, I had to trust that my driver knew the route like the back of his hand and could literally navigate it with his eyes closed. Floating trees, submerged glacial-sized rocks, and mirrors of sandbars created an obstacle course for us.

Halfway through the journey, thrashing waves cut our engine, leaving us at the mercy of the storm. The aging blue boat rocked violently from side to side. I was sure we would capsize. I thought seriously about the possibility of drowning in the Caribbean Sea. Planes were one thing—this dinky little scrap of wood was another.

What was I doing? Why was I on this boat during the middle of a storm risking my life for Rune? Where the fuck was I going to swim to if we wrecked?

The blackness of the night seeped into the blackness of the sea. Raindrops poured from the sky, bouncing off of the water. My naked eye couldn't find a separation. I tightened my grip, clenching my fists around the splintered wood, closed my eyes and tuned it all out. There was nothing I could do; we would either make it or not. I focused on keeping myself inside the boat. The cell phones were ringing off the hook the entire time.

Only by the grace of the universal spirit did we make it through the storm to Bastimentos Island alive. I paid the driver and he immediately turned around and bobbed into the darkness. The dock was empty.

My body turned to Jell-O and I threw off my backpack, gently lowering myself to the ground. I had been running on pure adrenaline and now that I was safe, my body shut down. That was okay with me. The group wasn't arriving until the next day and I knew how to deal with Rune.

I was already soaking wet, so I sprawled out across the old wooden dock on my back, looking up at the sky. The soft pitter-patter of rain hitting water sent chills down my spine. It was sublimely, almost deafeningly quiet, save for the one boat wafting Fleetwood Mac from its cabin windows. I considered that a nice addition to the evening. Beautiful stars gleamed through the ominous clouds, filling the sky. Panama stars. Island stars. I took a deep breath and closed my eyes. Alone in the night, I began to relax. Sometimes, nature is the best companion.

Then a cell phone rang. It was Tilda. It began again.

I mired up the mushy hills on a golf cart, making my way to the restaurant where Rune was enjoying the elaborate, gluten-free, corn-free, dairy-free barbecue dinner, prepared especially for Tilda. Since they were delayed in Panama City, things didn't work out as planned and Tilda refused to pay for the barbecue. That would be for me to figure out later.

Delivering Rune to his abode, I got stuck 'talking shop' until he released me at 12:30 am to mop the floors. After the last one was sparkling, I retreated to my room and found my luggage right where I left it in my haste earlier. Sitting down on the bed to prepare for the next morning, I leaned against the headboard to rest my eyes for just a moment.

At 5:00 am, I awoke to a tapping sound. Opening my left eye, bright sunshine pierced my vision. I winced and turned my head away. Scrounging around for one of the eight cell phones to check the time, I realized I was still atop of the comforter in my clothes. The group would arrive in two and a half hours.

"Rise and shine!" Rune screeched manically through the window.

"Hang on," I yelled.

He was waiting in the passenger seat of the golf cart when I made it outside after brushing my teeth. Assuming my role as driver, we went to breakfast where I ordered fruit, protein, and bottled water. The internet told me Bocas water was no good. Days before, Tilda instructed me not to worry about buying bottled water.

"The island water is good," she said sternly. What she really meant was not to spend her money buying myself bottled water. I bought a few cases of bottled water anyway. I didn't want to get sick.

Breakfast was spent tuning out Rune's work talk while simultaneously appearing engaged. I wasn't very hungry but if I had known how scarce food would become for me from then on, I would have been hoarding all the snacks. Busy escorting everyone to and from each meal and attending to their needs before, during, and after, the cafe on the island was always closed once I was relieved for the evening. As far as Tilda was concerned, the entire reason I existed was to make things easier for them, so I absolutely could not be absent to nourish myself.

After I dropped off Rune at his villa, I turned the golf cart right back around and went down to the dock to catch a water taxi to the airport. Everything went as planned, including griping from the guests about the heat, dirt, and how 'third-world' this third-world country was. The usual.

Transporting thirty guests by water taxi proved to be a challenge. Luckily, I met Ariel, a reliable Panamanian boat driver. He procured a second boat and made sure we made it without incident. I was still chided by Tilda for the grandparents being exposed to splashing water and a rough ride. Unbelievable.

Personally chauffeuring each guest to their villa, my next task was to organize and deliver luggage. A dusty purple truck dumped the bags and suitcases at the end of my driveway. I spent the next twenty minutes sorting through the pile in the middle of the dirt road.

Tilda sped up the driveway on a golf cart, splattering chalky mud all over me. She appeared to be transporting Elizabeth to my villa. Oh *hell* no.

Weeks ago, Tilda sent an email informing me that she had conceded and allowed me to have a private bedroom, as promised by Rune. Elizabeth would be sleeping in the den of another villa. Tilda then suggested that I offer to *share my bed* with Elizabeth. I completely ignored that email.

Entering the villa to find out what was going on, Tilda popped around the corner.

"Hey!" she sang in a baby voice. For whatever reason, smart, capable, bitchy Tilda chose to speak like a dumbed-down Paris Hilton most of the time. I first noticed it around Rune but then realized that she communicated with many people in that manner. It was so weird.

"Hi." I deadpanned, in a failed attempt to sound upbeat.

Elizabeth appeared, babbling like a toddler who had been

given too much sugar. Her spiraling curls bounced as she gestured wildly, screaming with her hands.

"Em! We're roommates again! Isn't it so great?" She grabbed my shoulders and shook me violently.

I shirked away, the invasion of my personal space really starting to bother me.

"But this time we get to cuddle!" She squealed and winked at me. My poker face failed, exposing my true feelings.

Jesus take the wheel, I thought to no one in particular.

Rain poured from the sky all week. Each day consisted of unrelenting, backbreaking manual labor accompanied by condescending treatment from the guests, if I received any acknowledgment at all. Ordering me around like a dog, or worse, treating me as an invisible second, third, or tenth-class citizen, I inched closer and closer to the edge. I was very good at biting my tongue, sucking it up, doing the work, and keeping my mouth shut. I was a middle-class American. That's what we do best. But they were about to cross the line and I was going to snap.

My cell phone buzzed around on the nightstand each morning between 4:30 and 5:00 am. Elizabeth consistently complained about my alarm, whining that it 'disturbed her sleep'. She wouldn't let it go, at one point taking it so far as instructing me to sleep on the couch in the living room so she could get her "beauty sleep." The audacity of the people surrounding me never ceased to amaze me.

As I reversed out of my villa driveway one night, I heard screams. Slamming on the accelerator, I high-tailed it toward the commotion. What I found was more annoying than shocking.

Guests were running around, blabbing that "Bobby tried to stab someone!" Bobby was Rune's dad. He must have had too much to drink during a sports fishing trip I arranged for him earlier that day. Rune placed me in charge of preventing stabbings. Bobby liked me for some reason, so I never felt threatened by him. However, his antics were stressful and required me to coddle him like a baby.

Rune's sister cornered me and thrust a handful of sweaty benzos into my palm, closing my fingers around them. "Here, take these. I know you need 'em, girl, dealing with all these snobby ass stuck-up motherfuckers," she said, referring to Tilda's kin's rude behavior but ignoring her own family's contribution to the madness.

Rune's sister herself was mostly crazy. Rune told me stories about her beating up her ex-boyfriends, stabbing them with screwdrivers. She was a bad-assed, foul-mouthed mechanic covered in tattoos with huge fake boobs and an even bigger personality.

She was definitely crazy. But she was lower class American crazy, not upper class elitist crazy, which are two totally different things. She had the capacity to be human and view me as a human as opposed to a servant—or at least hold conflicting views.

I accepted the Valium, grateful for a slight escape. Immediately popping one in my mouth, I washed it down with bottled water. The rest I secured within the zipper pocket of my backpack.

Running ragged, I was occupied from dawn to dawn, subsisting on bottled water, caffeine from extra Coca-Colas snagged from the villa fridge, and a few snacks I could grab here and there. I lost about ten pounds while I was in Panama, down to skin and bones when I returned to the States. The stress was inconceivable.

Tilda woke me from my sleep in the middle of the night to investigate a noise in her villa. Trudging over in my pajamas and determining the refrigerator as the culprit, I was dismissed to rest. Less than fifteen minutes later I received another call instructing me to return to her villa, unplug the refrigerator, ensure it was fixed the next day, and recoup any possible energy fees assessed during the time that the refrigerator was malfunctioning.

The absurdity didn't stop with Tilda. "For anything you desire, just ask Emily," Rune told the guests over and over.

They were quite the pair.

Tilda's brother's girlfriend was a tall, skinny ginger with an attitude problem. Deathly allergic to insects, especially fire ants, which were knowledgeably widespread on Bastimentos, she required doorstep-to-doorstep chauffeuring. Snubbing me the entire trip, she refused to speak to me directly. She was so bad-mannered, one of the absolute foulest, if possible to rate any of them worse than the other. They were all trifling.

Due to the shitty weather accompanying the cheaper off-season of the island, I became a food delivery service for each of the guests. Not wanting to leave the comfort of their villas, I was deployed to brace the storms and feed the village. Often sent traveling across the ocean to town multiples times per day to run frivolous errands, the guests' wishes and whims were sent to me via text, chasing me night and day.

One of Tilda's uncles took pity on me during a torrential downpour. Shielded from the rain beneath the porch, he offered me a smoke and a gin and tonic. I was stressed the fuck out. Lighting the cigarette, I inhaled deeply, soothing my raw nerves. Rune appeared out of nowhere, speaking to Tilda's uncle as if I wasn't there.

"She's fucking smoking? You know, she clearly can't make good decisions. I'm deducting five hundred dollars from her performance pay for each cigarette," he said condescendingly. "Unless you think I should make it more?"

I fucking hated him.

Elizabeth and I were drafted to attend a pre-wedding venue visit with Tilda. Tilda insisted I carry her over-sized, heavy suitcase full of bullshit all day. I was livid.

She was more than capable of carrying it herself, an avid runner and extreme athlete who had biked across the country and completed a plethora of competitive races, including a twenty-four-hour marathon. But she refused to touch the handle to her luggage. She truly thought she was better than me.

The taxi driver's music drowned out Tilda's bullshit during

the thirty-minute drive over sandy beaches and through the jungle to Playa Bluff. Haggling with the cab driver to the point of embarrassment, Tilda made him agree to wait at the venue for over an hour for free. This was not common practice; time is money everywhere. She refused to heed the suggestion of gifting the taxi driver with an ice cold Coca-Cola while he sat in the heat.

"He'll be fine." Tilda was such a stingy bitch.

We confirmed the details of the ceremony with the beautiful Cheyenne, half of a British couple who left their high-powered marketing careers in the UK for the slower pace of running a tiki-bar on the dreamlike beaches of Bocas.

"Our income is lower," she admitted, "but our quality of life has increased tenfold."

Cheyenne helped me so much. Connecting me to Panama musician Calypso Joe when he was unreachable in the islands, decorating the venue, and working with an outside bakery to fulfill Tilda's requests for an overly complicated cake that would adhere to her diet of no gluten, sugar, corn, or flour— Cheyenne made it happen.

Situated on a sandy beach, the open-air bar and lounge area featured elaborate wood carvings, fat tree stump tables, and a green felt-lined pool table. Everything was to Tilda's liking. I crossed my fingers that she would feel the same way the next day.

Waving goodbye to Cheyenne, our sweating taxi driver pulled away from the restaurant down the beach toward Bocas Town. The three of us shared a sufficiently awkward lunch, Tilda's uppity comments about the cleanliness of the neighborhood entered my ears as the muted trombone from Charlie Brown. I turned on Rune-mode, nodding and smiling on autopilot.

Elizabeth was on energy level ten. I ignored her. Tilda insisted on buying lunch but then watched over our plates like a hawk, ensuring no morsels were spared. She and Rune were perfect for each other.

The morning of the wedding, I awoke at 4:30 am. My total

sleep deficit was double digits. At this point in the trip I hadn't showered in quite a while. There was no time or reason. Stepping out of the door, I was covered in mud, clay, and sweat anyway. When I tried to shower one of the first days, I was interrupted four times by guests with questions. They were like infants.

I was supposed to fade into the background of the wedding anyway. Washing my face and brushing my teeth, I would try to squeeze in a quick rinse before heading to the ceremony, but for now I was living in about three days' worth of filth.

I picked up this dirtbag habit from my cool backcountry friends. Life was much more enjoyable when you weren't worrying about how you looked, or smelled, for that matter. Morning routines were quicker, and didn't involve any hair drying. Rune liked to say he was a true dirtbag but in actuality, he had become a spoiled little luxury hotel monger who bragged about wearing custom three piece suits hand-sewn by his tailor in Hong Kong. He soaked in Jacuzzi tubs. I roughed it.

Securing my golf cart at the dock, Ariel was to pick me up at 5:00 am sharp, which was very early, especially for island time. I prayed he would show.

Hanging out on the dock in the wee hours of the morning was enchanting. Serene. The soft sounds of unspoiled nature, water lapping and birds chirping, drifting gently from side to side. It never gets old.

Ariel was right on time. We greeted each other sluggishly as I hopped into the boat and sprawled out, kicking my legs up on the seat in front of me. Lighting a cigarette, I reclined and gazed off into the sky, mentally preparing myself for the day. I was already in a high state of annoyance due to Tilda's sister, Felicia.

The little priss lost her luggage. Through no fault of her own, I'll give her that. She was adhering to an extremely strict diet, of course, and her checked baggage contained the food she planned to eat while in Panama.

I had been sent to the airport multiple times to check on

her luggage. No dice. It sucked making all those trips and not having anything to show for it, but to tell the truth, I derived a sick sense of satisfaction watching something not go exactly their way for once. All fun was lost the previous evening when she received a call relaying that her luggage was available for pickup.

Felicia promptly informed *me* that *I* could pick up her luggage first thing the next morning. Six o'clock am, to be exact. She then turned to her sisters with a stiff smile. They responded with overly-polite fake enthusiasm. The entire family were fucking robots. The sterile manner in which they interacted with each other was so formal and detached.

It rained off and on the entire day, perfect karma for Rune and Tilda's nuptials. I was repulsed by them. They were despicable. No empathy or emotions, just hollow shells acting out scenes of imagined ideal lives. To quote Holden Caulfield, they were just a bunch of phonies. It was all a masquerade.

After I delivered the luggage, Felicia, Tilda, Elizabeth, and the moms headed to Playa Bluff. When it was time, I ushered the guests into two water taxis. Ariel and his friend took us to the wrong dock on the mainland. Nobody realized this until after the grandparents had been hoisted out of the boat. Everyone glared at me and began bickering about the complicated journey. I was so sick of their shit.

"Everything will be fine. I'll be right back," I said calmly, but beginning to panic on the inside. Once I was out of their sight, I sprinted to the dock where I caught Ariel just before he traveled out of earshot.

"ARIELLLLLLLLLLLL!!!" I screamed desperately as a last resort.

If I missed those guys, we were sure to be late for the ceremony. The wedding was, supposedly, the most important thing about this trip. I couldn't fuck that up or there would be consequences, worse than any I had experienced. I couldn't handle anything else. Ariel turned in my direction. I jumped up and down.

"Wrong spot!" I tried to tell him. His boat made a sharp a

U-turn, cutting through the choppy blue waves. It looked like he was calling the second driver on his cell.

Dropping us at the correct dock, it was time to locate the next vehicle for the last leg of our trip. Thankfully, the two black mini-buses I scheduled were just where they were supposed to be. I greeted the drivers with gratitude for being on schedule.

Performing a head count, I realized Nicky was missing. "Where is Nicky?" I asked.

I was trying to keep my cool, but that was proving to be incredibly difficult. Why couldn't these people just be mature adults and get themselves where they were supposed to be, when they were supposed to be there, without complaining or wandering off? Most of the guests were incapable of taking care of themselves, needing me to wipe their asses and sprinkle baby powder on them with a slap. It was absurd. I was in the *Twilight Zone*.

Nicky reappeared with a case of beer in hand, throwing cans into one of the mini-buses.

"Nicky." I spoke in a controlled, calm voice. He stopped and looked at me. "We are going to be late and I'm going to be pissed off. I need you to get into the fucking mini-bus. *Now.*"

His expression changed to one of a puppy in trouble as he scuttled off. I felt bad for being stern to the only nice one, but he was fucking up my timetable. I hopped in the bus.

"Vamanos!" I commanded our chauffeur.

The two mini-buses pulled off in tandem. They were overloaded, due to Tilda's refusal to spend the money on a needed third bus. Everybody was scrunched together, sitting on each other's laps. The grandparents looked less than pleased. All hostility was directed toward me.

I bore the brunt of the shitty situation, as usual, my seat the sunken down step on the floor between the bench and sliding door. It wasn't very safe. The Panama driving conditions were better than Thailand, but not by much. What could I do? Accustomed to the feeling of impending fatality, I relaxed into my death trap, reviewing the wedding day to-do list.

In addition to managing every detail of the event that day, from signaling Tilda when it was her turn to walk down the aisle, coursing reception dishes, monitoring the bar tab, and handling the musicians, I also was responsible for wrangling Bobby, ensuring he was included in the photos, didn't get too shitfaced, or cut anyone.

It took some time, but I successfully convinced him to participate in the family wedding photos. Bobby agreed on the condition that I would stand next to him. Elizabeth showed me the proofs after the wedding. I'm most prominent, as Bobby and I had to climb upon chairs in the back to be seen. I'll always laugh when I think of the fact that I'm the focal point of every part of Rune and Tilda's wedding memories.

Cheyenne spent a considerable amount of time to ensure Calypso Joe would perform at the wedding. His music was great and he mingled with the guests all night, performing requests on demand. Of course, Tilda lowballed his regular rate, then refused to let me tip him. I still cringe when I think about her display of crassness. I secretly slipped Cheyenne cash for her to pass on to Calypso Joe. She thanked me.

After Tilda cut the cake, everyone stood around stuffing their faces making small talk. Cheyenne's husband approached Rune.

"You have a beautiful bride. You must be happy—on cloud nine," he said, patting him on the back.

Rune shrugged, a blank look on his face. "I'm bored." Typical Rune.

The guests swam in the Caribbean Sea, built sandcastles on the beach, danced barefoot in the moonlight, and drank cocktails to their heart's content. Upon ingesting a few Manhattans too many, Tilda's dad, Big Tim, a geriatric in his seventies, asked me to bend over for him.

He was a typical mostly-absent upper class workaholic, clocking 100-plus hour weeks and often sleeping at the office throughout Tilda's childhood, leaving her with serious daddy issues. Prior to his three sheets to the wind status, Big Tim and I had a thought-provoking conversation about socio-economic impacts on long-term life satisfaction and the factor luck plays in the equation. Providing his email address, he asked me to keep in touch, interested in continuing our discussion.

"You're a smart woman and I really enjoy talking to you. We need more people like you in the world," he said, nodding in approval.

Tilda overheard the words she longed to hear her father say to her, daggers in her eyes. If she hadn't hated me yet, she did now.

The party died down and after taxi and boat trips, everyone had been safely delivered back to their villas. I didn't get to bed until 3:30 am. Elizabeth had long been asleep, taking up hers and my side of the bed. Ugh.

The day after the wedding I had errands to run in Bocas. Sleeping only an hour or two, I jumped awake before the sun, accustomed to the constant fight-or-flight state. My body had long ago switched over to an emergency, self-preservation mode.

The previous week destroyed me. Walking to the boat dock slowly, a bit dazed and confused, I made the decision to take a few hours for myself. In my pocket was a list of items to pick up for a party Rune and Tilda were throwing at their villa that evening, but those could wait.

Grabbing a bottled water and handful of fruit from a corner street stand in Bocas, I devoured it in one gulp. Noticing a nail salon, the staff was happy to see me, ushering me up a set of wooden stairs to a comfy recliner in a small air-conditioned room. A petite Panamanian girl named Maria began to give me a pedicure and I apologized for the terrible state of my feet. They were in beast mode, looking like a troll from my Mexican surfing escapades and muddy slave labor in Panama. She laughed.

I smiled guiltily and picked up a magazine. It was all in Spanish. Setting it down and closing my eyes, the next thing I knew, Maria was gently shaking me awake.

"You fell asleep," she giggled.

Bewildered and groggy, I fumbled for my purse and paid her in cash, tipping 150 percent. Stepping off of the tavern stoop into the town square, I looked down and noticed that Maria had taken the liberty to choose a color for my toes while I was sleeping. It was perfect for me: sherbet orange. I smiled, adjusting my backpack and headed out into the streets of Bocas with a small piece of happiness. It was the little things.

I stopped in a street market to retrieve party supplies. Maneuvering my backpack through the narrow aisles to the rear of the store where the fresh meat and seafood were located, a pungent aroma of rotting fish filled my nostrils. I ignored it, as locals insisted this was *the* place in Bocas town for the best fish. Quickening my step to the butcher, I switched to shallow breathing as I made my purchase for the fish fry Rune's dad would perform. I also picked up some beer, seasoning salts, and breakfast food before plopping my items down on the checkout counter.

As I trudged through town with fifteen additional pounds of bulky groceries, I heard a familiar voice in an English accent. Turning my head to the left, there stood Cheyenne.

"Oh my God, Emily!"

"Cheyenne! I'm so glad to see you!" We hugged. "I want to apologize for everything. For my boss and Tilda, and the guests, and their behavior. You guys were so great and . . ." I rambled on.

"Emily! No, don't apologize for them. They are, from what I can tell, absolutely terrible, unhappy people. You know, Rune emailed me this morning, demanding a refund for the open bar because they didn't feel their guests drank enough, they were unhappy with the food placement, complained about insects and the music and rain—and he threatened to sue me if I used any of the photos!" She shook her head. "I feel so bad for you that you have to be around them! They were just awful."

Gently grasping my shoulders, her eyes stared in mine. "You deserve better than that treatment. You should quit that job straight away. You can just come home with me and stay with us for a few days, relax on the beach. We'll make sure you get back to St. Louis." She was so kind. I wasn't crazy. Rune and Tilda and everyone else were.

"Thank you so much, Cheyenne, I really appreciate it. I'm quitting for sure, but I'm gonna stick out the end of this trip. Again, I'm so sorry you had to deal with them. I wanted to warn you from the beginning but I didn't know how."

"Emily, don't you worry your pretty little head. I'm fine. You just take care of yourself. Remember, we're just down the road if you can't take it anymore. You're always welcome."

I promised to visit if I returned to Bocas. Cheyenne was such a kind spirit. I hoped we would meet again.

Back at Bastimentos Island, my golf cart had been taken by a wedding guest. This wasn't the first time. I was pissed. With no other choice, I put one foot in front of the other and marched more than a mile up the hill through the clay quicksand, clenching my toes to keep my shoes on my feet, the sinking mud determined to claim them.

Twenty minutes later, legs covered in sludge, body drenched in sweat, and panting from the heat, I stood in the middle of the kitchen in Rune and Tilda's villa unloading groceries. I was parched, my tongue dry and gummy. I made the mistake of speaking.

"I'm thirsty," I said, immediately wishing I had kept my mouth shut.

Tilda sprang into action, eager to use me to fulfill her dumb ideas about drinking the water in Bocas. Of course her guests would drink bottled water, yet she insisted the Bocas water was safe for me. Filling a glass to the brim with tap water, she forced it into my weak hands.

"Drink," she said, assertively.

Starved of a proper meal for many days and devoid of treatment as a human being for much longer, I was beaten down psychologically and physically. Unsteady on my feet and seeing double, my body needed water right then or I felt I might keel over into a comatose state. They'd probably just leave me on the floor to die, stepping over my body to reach their organic cashews on the marble island countertop, complaining about the mess in the kitchen.

It was all too much. I drank.

The cool water immediately eased my cracked lips, refreshed my mouth full of cotton balls, and kept me alive for a few more moments.

"See? The water is fine. Have another glass."

Delusional with dehydration, I downed a second glass.

"What happened to your feet?" Tilda asked, looking me over and noticing the scars.

"I tore them up surfing," I answered between mouthfuls.

"Oh, you went surfing. So that's where you've been all those times we could have used your help." Now she was throwing shade.

"No. I haven't set foot in the water in Panama. It's from surfing with Saleem in Mexico," I said with a stone face.

"Oh. Your feet look terrible regardless. Now go pick up Calypso Joe." Done with me, her voice was curt as she turned away. That's just how it was with Tilda.

Rune was in a hyper mood that day, racing around on a golf cart, laughing maniacally. He stopped and offered me a ride. How nice. We rambled down the muddy path to the dock while he waxed poetic about leaving his high-pressure lifestyle behind.

"Kiddo, I want to have more down time to spend with Tilda. You've proven yourself. You're extremely sharp, devoted, dedicated, and a fucking crazy hard worker. I trust you."

He spoke without pretense.

"How would you feel about me making you President of Click!?"

But that was crazy talk.

Regardless if he was bullshitting or serious, it would just be another carrot on a string, dragged out for years with endless false hope. If he did follow through, I would be subject to being the figurehead of a flailing company run by a madman behind-the-scenes. He would never give up the reins entirely. And I was so over Click! and Rune's head games.

Fetching Calypso Joe involved taking a water taxi to an overgrown, barely-inhabited island, crawling through shrubbery to find a path to his shack then nudging him until he awoke. I managed to get him to Bastimentos and haphazardly strapped onto the backseat of a golf cart a sympathetic staffer so graciously lent me. Up the hill we went.

Once Calypso Joe was in place at the party, I went through a mental checklist: music, food, drinks, sparklers, glow sticks. All tasks were complete. I let myself off of code red, breathing a sigh of relief. Mentioning to Nicky I was feeling the onset of a stress headache, he insisted on performing a tension-relieving scalp massage.

"Relax," he commanded softly. I closed my eyes. His iPod was a mix of ambient grooves that soothed my mind. For a few moments, I wasn't in Hades.

The headache dissipated entirely by the end of his treatment. However, I wasn't feeling so great otherwise. A rumbling noise echoed from my stomach, and not because I was hungry. These weren't malnourishment growls. This was different. I felt queasy. I needed to get back to my villa *immediately*.

Rune granted my recusal request, taking the opportunity to chatter to guests about how he was doing me a favor by organizing Calypso Joe's return home because I didn't feel well. What a douche.

Once he gave me the green light I was gone, slamming the golf cart into reverse and darting out of the driveway backward. Every bump I hit on my high-speed trek caused me to almost lose control of the golf cart and the contents of my stomach. The Bocas water got me.

I fumbled to unlock the door to the villa, hopping from one foot to the other, clutching my stomach in agony as I sprinted to the bathroom. My entire body convulsed. I was sicker than I had ever been before. Every single bit of anything that was inside of me wanted to make its way out, in whatever way possible.

After about an hour of hell, I summoned all of my energy to shower. I could barely stand. Leaning on the tile wall, I allowed the water to pelt my shivering body for a few minutes before half-crawling naked down the hallway to the room where I would again be forced to sleep with Elizabeth in a double bed. I could have strangled Tilda for that.

After donning a clean pair of underwear, shorts, and a T-shirt, I popped two extra-drowsy gel tabs into my mouth, timidly washing them down with clean bottled water smuggled out of the villa refrigerator. The bottled water belonged to someone else, but it was mine now; Panamocalypse was cutthroat. I paused for a moment to see if I would puke up the pills. I didn't. Grateful, I snuggled up in the blankets, attempting to soothe my ravaged body with peace and quiet, drifting off into blissful sleep.

I awoke on my back lying perfectly still. Opening my eyes, the room was dark and the digital clock burned red displaying 3:00 am. Turning my head to the right, Elizabeth was miraculously contained to her side of the bed, fast asleep.

Something felt wrong. Something felt—mushy.

I started to sit up and realized what happened. *Holy fuck.* I had water poisoning and while knocked out under a spell of antihistamines, I shit myself. Not only myself, I shit the entire bed. *What. The. Fuck.*

I panicked and froze, my mind racing. How the fuck was I going to get out of this? I was sharing a bed with Elizabeth, of all people. If she found out, it would be over. There was no way in hell that she would not tell every single fucking person she knew, ten times. Exaggerating every detail all day long, groaning and moaning. No. I needed to fix this *right now,* and no one could ever find out.

When I travel I hoard towels to ensure I have a fresh one for those days when I *do* want to take a shower. Thankfully, I hid two extra towels in my nightstand. My mind was moving a million miles a minute as I inched out of bed at a pace that would have worn on the patience of a snail. There was nothing more important to me at that moment than making sure Elizabeth did not wake up.

Silently, almost motionlessly, I cleaned what I could. The mess was too large. Both sides of the towel were now destroyed and in need of disposal. Stretching out the second towel, I gradually lowered it to meet the stained sheet, adjusting it ever-so-slightly to properly conceal the horror beneath.

I held my breath and slowly pulled my side of our shared comforter up to the pillow, praying to God that Elizabeth didn't roll over and claim the other side of the bed as was the norm for her. She would be in for a surprise and there would be no way I could deny it.

I managed to grab a few pieces of clothing while tiptoeing out of the room. Scampering down the hall, Tilda's cousins lay sleeping on the couch in the den. Just what I needed, the possibility of more people catching me in the middle of covering up the fact that I pooped all over the bed.

Locking myself safely in the bathroom, I ripped off my tainted clothing and hopped in the shower, thoroughly sanitizing my body. I was dried off and dressed before I knew it, running on pure adrenaline. Every second I was away from the bedroom was a second closer to Elizabeth discovering my terrible secret. Pulling a continuous string from the toilet roll, I wrapped my balled-up pile of poopy clothes until it was white as snow. It was time to get rid of the evidence.

Quietly pulling the cold metal handle of the bathroom door toward me, I poked my head out, surveying the villa. The cousins were still asleep in their same positions on the couch. Seizing the opportunity, I shoved the toilet paper football under my right arm, striking the Heisman pose, and stepped out into the hall with one toe.

Aiming my sight on the couch for any sign of life, my heart skipped a beat. I could not be found out. Inching forward, my left foot came to rest on a loose board, causing a loud squeak. I froze, clenching my chest and biting my bottom lip so hard I tasted blood, my heart about to burst out of my rib cage. No movement. They must have let the kids drink wine at dinner again.

It was now or never. Half-skipping, half-sliding across the wooden floor in my socks, I noiselessly exited through the unlocked front door. Raindrops poured down around me. The cold liquid shocked my dehydrated skin. I reached the dumpster after a few minutes and tossed in my soggy toilet paper ball of evidence along with my mushy socks.

I crept inside past the sleeping cousins and eased myself back into my shared bed with anti-gravity like skills, anchoring the towel in place beneath me. I shimmied the thin sheet away from Elizabeth, positioning it between us to keep her from noticing the towel. If she saw the towel, she would want to know, she would *have* to know. She could not know.

I lay awake for hours, staring at the ceiling and pondering my life, vigilantly checking and rechecking the sheet's concealment of the fucked-up towel. Elizabeth finally awoke around 7:00 am.

"Oh, hey there! What are you still doing in bed? It's almost seven—you're normally up before five!" she smiled, curling toward me to cuddle. My mind shrieked with warning, every muscle in my body tightening as she moved in my direction.

"Hi, I'm not feeling well. I think I'm still sick," I responded, faking a cough, hoping she would fear contagiousness.

I was right. She immediately recoiled and rolled out of bed. I lay stoically, not daring to budge. It was awkward. I didn't move an inch and was in the same exact position when she returned from her morning shower, breakfast, and chat with the rest of the inhabitants of the villa.

She looked at me strangely.

"Are you okay? Do you need anything?" she asked with concern.

"No, I'm fine," I squeaked out. All I wanted was for her and everyone else to begin their day and get the fuck out of the villa so I could finish destroying the evidence and move on from this shameful experience in my life.

"Okay, well I'm heading down to the beach with the

cousins. I'll see you soon!" The door shut swiftly. Kneeling by the window, I watched them drive away in the golf cart. I could breathe again. Hopping into action, I did a sweep of the villa to ensure that I truly was alone.

Now the real work began. Stripping the bed of all sheets, blankets, and pillows, there was only enough room for one in the washing machine. Rapid action, I dumped the comforter into the hot soapy washer; the sheets would have to go. Stuffing them into a large trash bag, I ran to the dumpster again, this time even faster, as I was in broad daylight carrying soiled sheets.

The mattress did not come out unscathed. Struggling in the small room, I successfully flipped it after multiple attempts. The large brown stain I gifted it was now out of sight, never to be found again—or at least not until after we were gone.

The stars had aligned to allow this travesty to transpire on our last evening in the villas. This meant that everyone had already packed their things and checked out of their rooms leaving me free to roam throughout, snatching a loose sheet from the master bed, comforter from the guest bed, and fitted sheet from the pull-out couch. Mismatching those together, the bed would appear semi-normal upon check-out. I didn't care what happened after that.

A pickup truck rode around collecting luggage. I carelessly vaulted suitcases into the air and onto the bed of the pickup truck, no longer giving a fuck. Wiping sweat off of my forehead with the bottom of my blue tank top, I smiled. The worst was over. We were heading off that island in a few hours and back to Panama City.

I would see Dmitri again, which was intriguing. But mostly, I was looking forward to returning to St. Louis and cutting all unnecessary ties. While sick as a dog the night before, lying in my shit-stained bed, I decided I was done living my life for other people.

Plan or no plan, I was quitting my job. I would never again subject myself to anything like the Panama trip or Rune's wretched behavior. In fact, I was never going to do anything I didn't want to do—for the rest of my life.

I knew what had to be done.

As our flight landed at Albrook airport, I received an email from Dmitri inviting me to dinner, but I couldn't make it. A deep-cleaning shower was a must. We agreed to meet at Club Tantalo around 10:30 pm.

The group arrived at Hotel Sonesta in Panama City after 9:00 pm. The grandparents were exhausted and the kids were cranky. Ignoring everyone else's needs as usual, Tilda insisted on a post-wedding dinner at a Brazilian steakhouse.

I pulled Rune aside. "Rune, I'm not going to dinner. I need some downtime." I felt powerful making that statement, and even more powerful with the fact that I didn't care what he thought about it. I wasn't asking, I was telling.

He obliged with zero resistance. "Okay kiddo. Whatever you want." They headed off to the restaurant as I retreated into my hotel room.

Scrubbing off the grime from the harrowing week in the glass shower overlooking a view of the city, I lacked time and energy to mess with my hair, slicking it all up in a bun on the top of my head. My makeup options were sparse. Thankfully, I brought along mascara, eyeliner and blush. I didn't have to use much, as the tropical sun had toasted my skin evenly, like a done-just-right s'more roasted over a campfire.

I pulled on a silky purple sundress that bared my shoulders and grazed my thighs. It was the only dress I brought for the trip. Braless, I slipped on a pair of cotton pink bikini panties, a last-minute dollar store pick up on the way to the St. Louis airport, deciding there would be no need to bring any of my cute underwear. I was wrong. When packing clothes for the slave week in Panama, a new love interest was the furthest thing from my mind.

My favorite sandals, bright blue Tory Burch knockoffs purchased from the Underground Shopping Center during my first trip to China, fastened around my ankles, accentuating my new pedicure.

I had spent less than forty minutes with Dmitri, but knew it was synchronicity. I could feel it. Whatever it was, I wanted it. I added an extra coat of blackest black mascara to my lashes and squeezed gooey raspberry gloss onto my plump lips, working them together back and forth until they were sparkling in perfect symmetry.

Smiling at myself in the mirrors above me on the elevator ceiling, I was ready for an adventure. Gliding through the lobby with confidence, all heads turned in my direction. I was used to it, normally wishing I was invisible. That day, I was happy for the self-esteem boost before my reunion with mysteriously magnetic Dmitri. A doorman dressed in a teal and beige suit, complete with the classic bellhop hat scampered to open the door for me.

"Look at you. Going out?" he asked. He had seen me arrive covered in filth, looking like a gremlin. My present appearance was a big difference. I laughed in amusement.

"Thank you. Yes, Tantalo. I should have a taxi waiting," I said, smiling.

I had become pretty good at navigating around foreign countries. I was now venturing out alone in the dark to meet strangers late at night at a bar I had never been to in a city I had spent zero time in.

I told no one where I was going or who I would be with. I was free to do exactly as I wished. No one knew me. I had no past and the only thing that existed was the present, each moment created by me. My possibilities were endless. It was exhilarating.

The cab driver took me to Casco Viejo, through deadlocked traffic and mazes of tiny, crowded side streets. Dropping me off in front of Tantalo, he realized I was from America and advised me not to be out late alone as a female. If I had a dollar for every time I heard that. Such is life if you have a vagina.

Standing on the curb of the narrow cobblestone street surrounded by tall buildings, I checked the time. Looking up, Dmitri appeared, walking toward me and smiling. He was so much more handsome than I remembered. My heart skipped ten beats.

"Hi Emily. You look beautiful." He leaned in and hugged me hello, kissing me on the cheek. I smiled and flushed a rosy red.

Looking past him, I yelled hello to the other guests I met earlier in the week. He held the door for me and we made ourselves at home on the rooftop deck.

"What are you drinking?" he asked, his eyes blue as the Panama sky on a cloudless day.

After only eating a few scant meals in the past week plus the Bocas water poisoning, I was concerned about drinking alcohol. I asked for a glass of white wine, figuring I could sip on it for a while. Monitoring my alcohol intake would be key. The last thing I needed was to get blackout drunk with people I didn't know.

Dmitri and I spent most of the evening in close quarters learning about each other, yelling over the loud techno music into each other's ears while his hand rested on the small of my back as if it had always been there. We readily devoured new bits of information about each other, our eyes ravenous with growing desire.

The plumbers heckled us, smiling with their eyes wide. "Look at you two!"

We were displaying unusually affectionate behavior for two people who had just met.

Dmitri wandered off from time to time as he was still working, hosting a large group of people and needed to be social. I understood. Hanging out with the plumbers, I was good. I can get along with anyone.

One short plumber, Levi, was particularly hammered. He spilled my wine and his beer on me repeatedly. I went through four glasses of pinot, consuming a total of half of one glass. The rest was on my feet, legs, and dress. I was sticky but laughing hilariously when his wife bought me a lemon drop shot as a truce.

After we downed our shot, Levi approached me.

"Do you know the story of Dmitri Harris?"

I looked at him confused, scrunching my eyebrows.

"Huh?" I asked.

"Do you know who Dmitri Harris is?" he asked loudly, slurring his words and leaning toward me.

"Don't! Leave her alone," the wives nagged.

"Do you know who Dmitri Harris is?" he repeated, intent on having this conversation. The wives again attempted to intervene, but the tequila had taken over and it was clear that there was no stopping him at this point.

"Some dude I met on a boat?" I was perplexed, unsure of where he was going with this.

"Dmitri Harris is worth two hundred and fifty million dollars. And I can tell you two are fucking perfect for each other. So you guys need to just go off and have your million-dollar wedding and live happily ever after," he slurred, matter-of-factly.

The wives swarmed Levi, buzzing, "Why did you tell her that?!"

My mind whirred like a bike without a chain. I was a superb internet stalker, so I was already aware that Dmitri was a pretty successful businessman. His 'plumbing store' ended up being a multimillion-dollar family business where he held the position of Vice President. Emailing me from his work account, it wasn't hard to figure out.

However, the $250 million dollar figure threw me for a loop. I didn't care about money or material items but couldn't even begin to comprehend what $250 million dollars was, or what that meant regarding his lifestyle. I heard the number but glossed over it, not connecting the dots that Dmitri and I belonged to two starkly different social classes. I'm glad I didn't.

Dmitri and I drank, talked, laughed, and danced to the strong techno beats on the rooftop bar until late in the night. The stars were bright. Dmitri wrapped his arms around my waist and pulled me close to him, enveloping my heart in clovers.

"So are we going back to my place or yours?" Dmitri asked. I was slightly taken aback, yet intrigued. If anyone but him had said that to me, I would have immediately checked them. With Dmitri, it was different. He could say anything to me, and I would most likely respond favorably.

"What kind of girl do you think I am?" I asked with faux offense, smiling and batting my lashes flirtatiously. It was all bullshit. I was totally going home with him.

He quickly scaled back. "We're all just going to hang out and have a few drinks," he said, innocently. Faux innocently, I might add.

"Well, I don't want to go anywhere near my hotel. The entire wedding party is there and I don't want to have anything to do with them tonight."

"Okay, we'll go to my place," he said decisively. Wrangling the others, we made our way to the elevators. Dmitri held my hand in his as he guided me downstairs, looking back at me every so often, smiling. My heart was spinning.

He hailed a few taxis for everyone. "Don't get in the cab with them!" a plumber's wife yelled to Levi as she pulled him away from us.

We slid into the taxicab and Dmitri instructed the driver to head to Playa Bonita. He was very in-charge the whole evening. I liked it. The entire backseat was open but our bodies were pressed together tightly. Hotel California hummed from the speakers as we passed the Panama Canal. Smiling at Dmitri, I sang.

"You have a beautiful voice. I knew you would," he said.

Dmitri looked at me and my body was electrified. The world sat in suspense of what was to come. I was short of breath. There was an undeniable connection between the two of us that was spontaneously combustible through eye contact.

Our lips touched. Warm, searching, wet, he tasted sweeter than ripe watermelon on a hot day. His energy was unlike anything I had ever felt. Tugging hair, biting lips, groping through clothes, hands between thighs, it was full on in the back of the cab. Every few seconds we would break away and stare deeply into each other's eyes. Then carnal behavior would commence once again. Arriving at the hotel we walked hand-in-hand, eye-to-eye through the lobby down an open-air hallway straight to his room.

Picking up where we left off, we kissed passionately. Taking a breath, he pulled back, a look of amazement on his face.

"Oh my God, you are so beautiful. If we had kids, they would have the most beautiful eyes ever," he asserted before covering my mouth with his.

Coming up for air, I asked breathlessly, "Do you want kids?"

Without breaking our rhythm, he responded, "Not now. Do you?"

"Same. Not now." Our lips met again. "Are you religious?"

He looked at me, hesitating, "Averagely. Are you?"

"I'm not religious at all," I said, blatantly.

"I'm not either," he confessed. It was adorable. Wrapping my hands around his neck, I pulled myself toward him. We dove back into each other. The sensation was unreal. Stopping abruptly, his expression was one of wonder.

"I feel so comfortable with you." He gazed into my eyes. "It's like I've known you forever."

Taking off his shirt he then pulled my dress over my head, noticing the tattooed black script on the inside of my right ankle. Grabbing my foot, he read intently.

"What does this mean?" he demanded.

"It's lyrics from *Hey Jude*," I answered. His beautiful mouth took the shape of a wide smile.

"You're incredible. Come here," he said, pulling me toward him. He couldn't look away, beginning to speak but trailing off before completing his sentence, hypnotized, murmuring, "Your eyes," over and over. He saw the ocean.

We were both naked. I suddenly remembered Saleem. I didn't feel bad or want to stop. I was at peace with the fate of our relationship. Dmitri and I had a real connection and I wanted him to know the truth before things went too far.

"I have a boyfriend," I blurted out. He looked at me

confused, as I'm sure he must have been.

"Why didn't you tell—"

I cut him off mid-sentence. "I'm not happy."

In our strange, perfect dimension of space in Panama, that was all I needed to say. He seemed to accept that answer.

"Well, I don't take any shit," he said gruffly, kissing my neck.

My body went weak instantly. He felt so good on top of me. Struggling to remember to breathe, I gulped for air.

"What do you mean?"

"Just so you know for the future."

My brain snapped out of the vanilla sky. He said future. Could there be more than Panama?

"Do you have a girlfriend?" I asked.

"No," he said without hesitation.

"Why not?"

"I'm really picky."

His stare made me weightless and I fell into him. At the last-minute my practical side kicked in. "Wait, do you have a condom?" I asked.

"No," he deadpanned, not slowing down at all.

"What?"

"No, I don't have a condom." He didn't seem deterred.

"What?" I asked again, surprised.

He spoke with purpose. "No, I don't have any and I don't want to use one with you anyway."

I looked at him in skepticism, then ran over to my bag. Always be prepared.

Dmitri and I made the most exquisite love, our bodies clinging to one another desperately. We never broke our gaze except when my pupils rolled in the back of my head, an action I couldn't control.

"Dmitri, I can't feel my fucking face."

He smiled in satisfaction and intertwined his fingers with mine.

Our breath exhaled in sync and we were dripping in sweat. He touched me tenderly, cradling my chin while gently pressing his lips against mine. His crystal blue eyes pierced my soul, demanding submission. I readily conceded.

"Nobody has ever looked at me the way you do," I gasped breathlessly. Life poured from his eyes, drenching me in love, desire, and respect. Every moment with him was the epitome of ecstasy. Making love to Dmitri was the best high, better than any synthetic one I had ever felt.

Afterwards, he spooned me, adorning my naked body with soft kisses and playing with his hands in my hair until we fell asleep. My alarm was set for 5:00 am, giving me enough time to prep Rune and Tilda's guest itineraries for the day. Most of them were heading to the airport that very morning so it wouldn't take long. I wanted it done and out of the way so I could enjoy the rest of my weekend in Panama, possibly with Dmitri.

The alarm beeped and I leapt out of bed. Pulling my purple-checkered dress over my head, I searched for the dollar store underwear. I spotted the pink panties on the floor and quickly slid them on. He popped up, wiping his eyes.

"Why are you in such a hurry?" he asked, distraught.

"I have work to do."

"This early? You should just come back to bed with me for a while," he smiled invitingly, patting the heap of down blankets next to him, "we can order breakfast."

It was more than tempting. Lying next to Dmitri soaking up his energy was heavenly. My soul perfectly calibrated, it was an overpowering, yet calming feeling. It was so heavy and pure. If there was such a thing as love at first sight, this was it.

"I wish I could," I said wistfully, as I leaned over the edge of the bed, lacing up my fifty-cent sandals. For the first time in my life, I really meant that statement. But I had responsibilities to take care of first. I was determined to end my time at Click! with integrity and finish out the trip. Hopefully I would be back in his bed later in the evening. Stuffing my phone in my bag, I looked at him and smiled with regret. "But I have to go right now."

"I wish you didn't. What are you doing later?"

"Not sure. I'll text you when I'm finished with work."

"Okay. Do you have money for a cab?" he asked, reaching for his wallet.

His concern amused me. Did he think I was stupid enough to go out into the middle of Panama without money to get back to my hotel? However, the fact that he cared enough to ask made me feel warm and tingly all over. I could take care of myself, but was long overdue to meet a man who would take charge for a while.

"Yes, I do, thanks though." I walked over to the bed, kissed him on the lips and smiled again, realizing my cheeks were hurting. I couldn't stop smiling. Dmitri made me feel alive. I would never get enough of him. I wanted to feel like that all the time.

The hotel staff arranged a cab for me. I was besotted, staring out the window at nothing, lost in my mind replaying the previous evening over and over. Feeling every intimate look, the electricity when our lips met, perfect fit of our naked bodies knotted together, and the undeniable energy between us. It was like a dream except it had taken place in the tangent reality. I couldn't believe it.

Slinking into the room Elizabeth and I shared, I hopped into the shower and dressed, switching on my laptop. After sending emails with guest checkout and flight information, I grabbed a bite to eat and texted Dmitri.

E: *Hey, I'm done with work for the day. What are you up to?*

He responded almost immediately.

D: *Went back to sleep for a while, getting up now. What were you thinking?*

E: *I was thinking I'd like to get to know you a little better and see you naked again . . .*

D: *I'd like to do that, too. What hotel are you at again?*

E: *Hotel Sonesta*

D: *Ok, I'll be there in about 20 minutes.*

A love-struck grin covered my face from ear to ear. Elizabeth wouldn't shut up about it. I guess I couldn't shut up about him. It was so unlike me. I couldn't wait to see him again; my heart was going to explode.

Rune, Tilda, Nicky, and a few others were hanging out in the hotel lobby. I appeared in retro high-waisted navy button up jean shorts, a skimpy midriff top that matched the turquoise tint of my eyes, trusty blue sandals, and my curly hair swept to the side in a low ponytail. Everyone stopped and stared at me. It was impossible for me to go unnoticed.

I knew Dmitri would walk into the lobby, as opposed to texting me when the cab was close. He was a gentleman. This was a problem. Nobody could see me with Dmitri. They all personally knew, or knew of, Saleem.

I nervously kept my eye on the door while engaged in conversation with Tilda about their Brazilian steakhouse visit. After a few minutes, I saw Dmitri enter the lobby out of the corner of my eye. In the middle of Tilda's sentence, I abruptly stood from the chair, pivoted sharply and darted through the front door, smiling as I passed Dmitri. He followed me.

I didn't excuse myself from our conversation or say goodbye to Tilda. I just left. It was rude but I was far past giving a fuck what she thought. My main objective was to exit the hotel without revealing my companion or whereabouts.

We power walked down the street and around the corner a safe distance. I relaxed and looked at Dmitri. He was dressed casually, wearing black board shorts, a gray T-shirt, and black sunglasses. On his feet were flip-flops. He was still the most handsome man I had seen anywhere in the world. His energy overtook mine and for once, I didn't mind. I wanted to soak it all in.

He looked at me with his blue eyes and smiled.

"Hi."

Oh God, that smile. The solar system lived in his eyes. They made me feel faint.

"Hi," I grinned back, showing all of my teeth and then some.

He hailed a cab. Hopping in, a wave of excitement washed over me. I couldn't believe I was lucky enough to be out with this guy again. He was so gorgeous, so smart, so capable.

We took the cab driver's recommendation for a coffee shop and he dumped us out by the waterfront. Dodging speeding cars, we dashed across the four-lane roadway to the entrance on the corner. It resembled an American fifties diner, with a large metal counter and cushioned bar stools.

Dmitri ordered coffee for us in halted Spanish; black for him, cream for me. The Panamanian diner clerk splashed black coffee into two small white paper cups and plopped them down in front of us, motioning to the condiment caddy to my right. He then slid a hand-written bill toward Dmitri. I snapped it up before he had a chance to object.

"I got it!"

"No, I'll take care of it," he reached for the blue and white striped check. I pulled it close to my chest, out of his reach.

"No way. I owe you for the boat ride," I said defiantly, pulling cash out of my bag.

"Fine, you can pay for the coffee, but I'll get the tip," he compromised.

I was tickled and thought his demeanor about the coffee was so very cute, but I was not budging.

Chuckling, I said, "No, it's okay; I can get the tip, too."

"Are you sure?" He sounded distressed, his blue eyes searching mine for confirmation.

I matched his gaze and felt an electric shock coursing throughout every cell of my being. God, I wanted to fuck him. Turning away, I released the breath I didn't realize I was holding.

"Yes, I'm sure," I said as I threw a few dollars on the counter.

We took our coffee to go and walked toward Panama's Old Town holding hands, a potent love spell cast upon us. Lost on the winding streets of Casco Viejo, we talked and talked, with Dmitri stealing kisses from me in the middle of our sentences.

He was exactly everything I had no clue I was looking for. He knew everything I didn't know and vice-versa. Dmitri was my true equal in terms of attractiveness, intelligence, energy, and multidimensional qualities. I had found my yin.

A double black-diamond skier, he was a Harvard alum, avid cyclist, surfer, hockey player, world-traveler, SCUBA diver, amateur photographer, wine connoisseur, pilot like his father, and Rolling Stones groupie, flying around the world to see them perform over and over again. He was so incredibly smart. Smarter than me. It turned me on more than anything in the universe. Regal, commanding, timelessly gorgeous, value-oriented, self-motivated and successful, our paths crossing were not just happenstance. Centuries are what it meant to me.

"I want to know more about you. What kind of music do you listen to?" he asked.

"Oh, I pretty much love everything except for most country."

"Johnny Cash?" he looked worried.

"Of course," I assured him. "But old school hip-hop is my favorite."

"Hip-hop?"

"Yep. The Beastie Boys are my Rolling Stones."

"The Beastie Boys, eh? I used to be really into Beck when he came out. Does that count?"

His attempt to relate was endearing. My face softened into adoration as I grabbed his arm and leaned into him, inhaling his scent.

"Yeah, that counts," I said, unable to repress a deep-set smile, my cheeks glowing from happiness.

We both liked to read. His current book was about Steve Jobs. Mine was about aliens.

"I mean, with how vast and expansive the universe is, it's ridiculous to think we're the only intelligent life form. The only one? No way. I totally believe in aliens. . . . You probably think I'm crazy now, don't you?"

He looked at me earnestly. "No, I like critical thinkers," he replied without missing a beat. No matter how stupid my stories, he still wanted more.

"I feel like I'm talking too much. Your turn," I said.

Shaking his head violently side to side, he brushed off my request. "No, no, I don't want to talk about me. I want to know everything about you," he said, squeezing my palm.

My heart glittered in twenty-four-karat gold. Nobody had ever taken the time to really get to know me. I couldn't believe this beautiful, charismatic individual wanted to.

We had a lot of things in common, but our most similar traits were our sense of adventure, love of learning, passion for life, and drive to achieve. We also both shared an inconceivable feeling of comfort with and strong attraction to each other. It was a perfect match.

Oh, I had been in love before. But this. This was different. It was the most authentic emotion I had ever expressed.

People say once your mind has been expanded, it can never contract. I now believe the same about the heart. Once I felt that feeling, I knew I would never go back again. My relationship with Saleem, or any of my former significant others for that matter, could never come close to the overwhelming sense of euphoria I felt when I was with Dmitri.

He chose a quaint cafe, Casco Pescaco, where we shared fresh lime ceviche and Panamanian beer beneath a red and white parasol while dining al fresco on the charming Plaza Bolivar. Our lunch conversation was schizophrenic, spanning movies, passions, drugs, work, travels, families, ménage-a-trois, politics, and more.

He asked my opinions. He listened to my words. He looked into my eyes.

"You should be a writer," he asserted.

I would never forget that moment of confirmation. Coming from Dmitri, it meant more than any other encouragement I had ever received.

"I've always wanted to be," I responded, my eyes exposing my soul to his.

"Come to Argentina with me," he said, grasping my hand.

I suddenly remembered the mess left to clean up with Rune and Saleem - my real life. I couldn't just pick up and go to Argentina with Dmitri. Of course I wanted to. But I couldn't. Not now.

"Ahh, I would love to go with you Dmitri, but I can't. I

have a job and some things to take care of," I said stupidly.

"So? Just come with me."

"I can't, really. . . . It's a little hard to explain but any other time than right now, I'm down," I said, shaking my head apologetically. Not going to Argentina with Dmitri would soon become one of my life's only regrets.

We wandered around the city for hours with our bodies intertwined, living a Stevie Wonder song every three minutes and thirty-three seconds. Stopping every so often to lean against a crumbling Casco Viejo wall, we embraced in its shade, displaying our kiss to the world. Making our way down the Amador Causeway, we couldn't stay away from each other.

It was the middle of the day, with runners and bikers and tourists enjoying the sun. Dmitri sat on the edge of a large fountain in the circle center. I stood with his strong arms around me. We kissed passionately, ignoring the onlookers. We didn't care. That moment we shared was all that mattered; we could see nothing else. Our vision faded past each other's aura, illuminating only us. The energy generated couldn't be ignored, our pheromones black holes, frying our brains and tuning our bodies to only one frequency, with no hope of escape.

Pressing his soft lips against my neck, he sent a chill down my spine. "We need to go back to my hotel," he whispered in my ear, glancing down at his stretched board shorts. I laughed, eyes gleaming, and grabbed his face, kissing him through my giant smile.

I hailed a taxi from the busy intersection, waving him over and giggling uncontrollably as he tried to run from the fountain to the cab without everyone seeing how aroused he was. Sliding into the backseat, he turned to me.

"Oh, you think that's funny?" he teased playfully, raising an eyebrow. He pounced on me with a devilish grin and I squealed in excitement. Kissing and touching, we stopped ourselves repeatedly on the way to the hotel, trying to keep calm and be respectful of the taxi driver. Obsessively locked into each other's eyes, we attempted to chitchat about the Panama Canal as we drove past it for the tenth time.

"Have you been to the canal yet?" he asked, holding my thighs.

"No, I haven't had time to go by there yet. Have you?" At this point, his hand was up my shorts.

"Oh really? You should go sometime." He grinned mischievously. "It's worth it."

I breathed heavily, my chest visibly heaving up and down, never breaking my gaze but failing to keep my composure. I grabbed his face, impatiently bringing his lips to mine. He slid his warm fingers inside of me and I melted all over him. I wanted to rip my clothes off in the back of that dirty cab.

He guided me through the lobby to his room with his hand wrapped around my exposed waist, fingers running slightly beneath the fabric of my shirt, pulling at my skin. As the door swung shut, we were naked on his bed again. Our lovemaking was even more divine, sprawled out under rays of sunlight shining in from the balcony overlooking tropical paradise.

My emotions were lucid, my heart open. I gave Dmitri everything I had to do with as he wished. My body, my mind, my soul. I surrendered it all to him as I had never done before. He was everything to me.

Catching our breath, Dmitri and I shared a bottle of water while we snuggled in bed. "Ahh, this is cozy," he said, wrapping the fluffy blankets around us. He was so warm. It felt so perfect. "I can't believe the feeling I have when I'm with you, Emily. It's crazy. I've never felt anything like it. You make me so comfortable." He nestled his face into the nape of my neck, kissing me gently, sending a euphoric jolt down my spine, visible as goose bumps on my body.

"Ditto," I said, radiant from the inside out on a cloud nine-hundred-and-ninety-nine-thousand high. I leaned back into him, our naked bodies pressed against each other.

"Again?" I asked.

"I'm too old, let's take a nap first." He was serious.

"Okay," I agreed happily. Closing my eyes, I breathed into him. We napped, made love, lounged in bed playing with each other's hair, and repeated until the sun faded into the ocean.

He had business to attend to early evening and began to dress for his meeting.

"Would you like to have dinner with me tonight?" he asked, his blue eyes lighting up.

"Of course." My eyes mirrored his. He planted a big kiss on my lips. I couldn't stop grinning.

"Emily, you know I'm more than just physically attracted to you, right?" he asked, his brow furrowed, eyes probing mine. I could already feel his strong emotions but they were a delight to hear.

"Yes, I know. I'm more than just physically attracted to you as well, Dmitri." Wrapping my arms around him, I continued, "but I am *extremely* physically attracted to you."

He squeezed my ass and kissed me hard. "I wish I didn't have this meeting and I could just stay with you," he said, running his hands over my body.

"Me too. But work is work." He agreed, kissed me goodbye, and off I went, floating back to my hotel.

Elizabeth insisted I fill her in, awestruck by the sudden love story. Rustling through her bag, she produced a brand-new pair of lacy black panties with the tags still on them. Gifting them to me, I was touched by her kindness. That marked the beginning of our friendship, on my side, at least.

I received a text from Dmitri asking if I was okay going to dinner with him and his entire family, as they were all in Panama for the business trip. I was taken aback. This whole situation was insane. And I loved it. I replied.

That's cool.

He replied that they would pick me up in about twenty minutes. I perfected my makeup, wearing the same outfit from earlier. It spent most of the day on the floor in Dmitri's hotel room anyway.

Standing outside Hotel Sonesta waiting for Dmitri to pick me up, I was nervous. Meeting his family was huge. This was all happening so fast, it was crazy. It felt so right. The taxi pulled up and the door slid open. Five faces stared back at me. I smiled and said hello, hopping in while the driver slid the door shut.

Dmitri introduced me to his parents, Peater and Lillian, and brother and sister-in-law during the fifteen minute ride to the steakhouse. They shared his kind eyes and warm demeanor. Taking my hand, Dmitri escorted me to a big round table, pulling my chair out and helping me into my seat.

The restaurant was swanky. Seated to Dmitri's right, he was the host of the evening, ordering a wine pairing for each course, inquiring about my preference before committing. Sneaking doting glances to each other throughout the meal, I knew we had done this before, somewhere in another lifetime.

Dainty appetizers were presented to us as Dmitri's family laughed about his inability to cook.

"Do you cook?" he asked, leaning in toward me.

Engaging in his side conversation, I responded, "No, I don't enjoy cooking. I like to bake."

His brow crumpled in confusion. "But how do you eat?" he asked.

"How do *you* eat?" I asked, arching an eyebrow playfully.

His mom interrupted our exchange. "So, Emily, you like to bake?"

Winking at Dmitri, I smiled and turned back to the table, working my magic for the next few hours while his family softly interrogated me about my life, job, education, interests, hometown, even the immaculate style of my handwriting. Peater and Lillian were ultra-perceptive, their inquiries meant and my answers understood on more than one level.

The extent of wealth in Dmitri's family became more obvious during dinner. Aside from their upper-class vocabulary, formal dinner manners and attire, the conversation made things clear. Dmitri's sister-in-law recanted a story of how they were dropped off at the wrong mall earlier in the day. Tittering with hilarity, she explained how they finally made their way to the correct mall, so she could do her Louis Vuitton shopping. We were definitely living in different worlds.

However, one of my most useful skills was the ability to be a chameleon. I can fit in anywhere. Charming them with my intellect, humor, diversity, and smile, the six of us got on very well.

Saying our goodbyes to his family after dessert, Dmitri and I headed out onto the moonlit streets of Panama City in search of jazz music. He maneuvered himself to walk closest to the road, shielding me protectively in his arms as we passed shady looking street characters, concerned for my safety. I wasn't used to that. I was head over feet, with nothing but stars in my eyes.

Dean Martin's inebriating *Sway* pulled us onto the patio of a local cantina, dimly lit with a string of fading colored-paper lamps. Hiding away on one bench at a corner table, Dmitri's lips became stained red from the strawberry daiquiri on mine. A glimmering constellation in the velvet sky demanded our attention. Resting my head on his shoulder while taking in the blanket of gems above us, it was all surreal.

"Why are you single?" I asked outright. "Are you like a super player?" I was laughing but very serious.

"What? No!" he exclaimed, offended. "Why would you think that?"

"I'm just kidding . . . sort of. But I mean, for real . . . why are you single?"

"Well, I was in a four-year relationship that was doomed from the beginning. We were always fighting. It was never going to work out so we eventually broke it off. Then one day I turned around and I was thirty-six and single." He took a sip from his drink. "What's up with your situation?" he asked.

I shook my head slowly, lowering my eyes to the table. "My relationship . . . was over a long time ago, I guess. I've just been delaying the inevitable. It's a sad situation." I didn't know what else to say, so I just sat in silence.

Recognizing my internal struggle, he placed two fingers under my chin and lifted my face to his, kissing me until I felt dizzy.

"You deserve happiness. You're such an amazing person. You have this energy, this enthusiasm, the way your eyes light up . . . no, even when you were talking to my family. I was watching you. I've never met anyone like you. You're so passionate and real and beautiful. You're incredible."

His eyes burned through me, an infinity of energy captured between us, bouncing back and forth from one body to another, recharging and building up with each cycle until our brains short-circuited from overload of electricity. The connection was beyond our control.

"*You* are incredible. This feeling is incredible. I can't even look at you, Dmitri. I'm so attracted to everything about you. I just want to get naked and jump on top of you. Right. Now." He didn't need me to tell him twice.

"Let's get out of here." Throwing cash on the table, we hopped in a cab for another inappropriate ride to his hotel.

Naked on his bed, the phone rang. It was well into the evening, past midnight. The front desk was calling to inquire about Dmitri's 'late-night companion,' which was me. They thought I was a prostitute. Dmitri was not pleased. I hadn't seen the hookers in Panama City so I couldn't tell if it was an insult or not.

Meeting them in the lobby, the staff made it clear that his room was only registered for one guest and he would have to pay a couple hundred dollars for me to stay with him. Dmitri was pissed. It wasn't about the money; he paid it without a second thought. But then he let them have it.

"This is absurd. You have offended both me and my guest. You must not be aware that I've filled the majority of your hotel rooms with my company's conference." His tone was seething. "I can't believe you called me about this at all, nonetheless in the middle of the night. Insulting my guest and making us come down here. I can tell you we won't have a conference here again with treatment like this."

He fell just short of asking if they knew who he was. It was epic. But I just wanted to get back in bed with Dmitri. We only had a little bit of time left.

A midnight storm raged outside the open balcony doors as we made love. We stayed awake together all night, smiling, cuddling, kissing, and looking into each other's eyes as much as we could.

"Who are you?" I marveled in wonder as he tenderly caressed my face, brushing a lock of hair from covering the blue of my eyes and tucking it behind my ear.

He nuzzled his face against mine, murmuring softly. "Who are you? And where you have been all my life?"

I hadn't been anywhere.

It felt like only five minutes passed when the front desk called to inform me my cab had arrived.

"I miss you already," I said as he hugged me.

"I don't want you to leave," he declared.

"I don't want to leave either but I have to right now," I said, my words heavy with regret.

Dmitri tried one more time. "Just stay in Panama and go to Argentina with me," he urged, his eyes pensive.

"You know I can't. I mean, not right this moment, anyway. I have an entire life to tend to." I looked at him with sadness in my eyes, hoping he understood.

We kissed and said our drawn-out goodbyes as the phone rang off the hook, the taxi driver growing impatient. Stepping into the open-air hallway, his hotel door clicked shut behind me. Showers poured down, dousing my clothing into dead weight and slowing my step as I struggled against the grain toward the elevator. Standing in the torrential rain, my heart told me to go back. I couldn't just leave my soul mate like that. I wouldn't.

Turning around, I ran back, banging on his door with wet hands. It opened straightaway as if he had been waiting for me to return. We grabbed each other, his hands gripping my cheeks, kissing me hard as if his oxygen was the only thing that kept me alive. At the time, it was. We ran our hands over each other's faces, desperately attempting to commit each other's every curve and freckle to memory. We couldn't tear ourselves apart.

"I'm going to miss my flight," I murmured in between kisses and gasps for air.

"I know. You should go," he said, holding me tighter.

"I don't want to." I wrapped my arms around his neck.

"I don't want you to either." He picked me up and put me on the bed. Lost in each other again, we fed off of the love streaming around us.

The phone rang nonstop. After a few minutes I came to my senses. My taxi was downstairs, I was already late, and still had a twenty minute ride to the hotel. My heart sent warning shocks throughout my body as I tried to uncouple myself from his arms. I was supposed to stay. I knew it. I could feel it. I belonged with this man. But I couldn't.

"Text me to let me know you get home safe," he said, kissing me gently.

"Promise." My pillowed lips pressed against his with purpose, channeling my energy to him through my mouth. We held hands as I left, stretching our arms until they no longer reached, never breaking our gaze, me walking backwards in the rain until I could no longer see him. My heart strained with every step.

Back at the hotel, I had no time. Elizabeth and Nicky were already loading their luggage into the taxi.

"Where have you been, girl? We gotta go!" Nicky exclaimed.

"Yeah, hurry up and get your shit, Emily!" Elizabeth was not a morning person.

"Be right down!" I yelled as I ran past them into the hotel lobby. Returning with my backpack and passport, I hopped in the taxi, ready to go home and flip my entire life upside down.

8 PITY THE POD

The cortege home from Central America was quite dramatic. I was overwhelmed with the extreme ups and downs of the past week. The tough decisions had been made and I was secure with my reasons, but still had to execute.

Pushed to my limit, immense self-reflection had taken place. Everything was about to change. The previous year's experiences were necessary prerequisites to prepare me for my transformation. A mirror held to my life, presented as a series of impossible-to-ignore events, forcing me to assess my existence as it was and could be.

It was *the moment* when everything became clear.

The challenges I faced and conquered confirmed to me once again that I was capable of absolutely anything. I was no longer worried about what-ifs and consequences of deviating from the normal American lifestyle. I didn't know what was going to happen after that, but it didn't matter anymore.

In Panama, something clicked. The right electrical paths connected in my brain, fusing together permanently. I finally realized that I was the engineer of my life. I only had one life and it was solely mine to design. Top to bottom, left to right, head to toe, soul to stars.

I no longer wanted to live as a bystander, a paper-pushing

worker bee in the background, turning on the lights each morning so the rest of the world could shine. I didn't want to be a slave to the Matrix. I wanted to really live. I wanted to create. Create what? I didn't know yet, or maybe I always knew. At the time, the world and exactly what it had to offer me was a fleeting enigma that I would catch a rare glimpse of as it rushed across a busy street, disappearing into a sea of people on the boulevard. I knew it was out there.

In the past I had been locked in a box, surrendering the freedom to be myself in exchange for a cookie-cutter life with set milestones for each decade. I let society define me, mitigating all risk and innovation. Steady and stable won the race.

I now viewed life as a blank canvas and was ready to live in color. I was the artist, paintbrush in hand and palette with infinite dreams in vibrant shades by my side. Within me, the burning passion and desire to create my masterpiece. Fear had admitted defeat, realizing it had lost its power over me. I was ready to live life on my terms, although I didn't know yet exactly what that meant. I was determined to find out.

Rune wouldn't be back in the states for a few days, so I would deal with him later. However, immediately upon returning to St. Louis, I had to complete the quite messy task of breaking up with my completely unsuspecting live-in boyfriend. Over the years we discussed a location for our wedding, opened a joint bank account, and shared the same bed at night. Now I wanted out.

Tortured with guilt, my stomach was in knots, causing me to vomit in the stinky airplane bathroom. I wanted to press fast-forward on my life that day. My decision to move on from our relationship would affect him emotionally and financially. Those worries, combined with societal pressure, kept me in that relationship long past its expiration date.

Elizabeth's boyfriend, Britton, offered to drop me off at home and I gladly accepted. As we waited for our luggage, I received an email from Rune. He and Tilda were completely unsatisfied with every single aspect of their trip to Panama, especially the wedding. I was instructed to halt all payments to vendors and solicit full refunds.

I momentarily freaked out, then remembered I didn't give a shit anymore. I was done with Rune and Click! and ignored the accumulating emails.

I was perched on the couch when Saleem entered the house. I asked him to sit down then blurted it out. We had grown apart, seeking contradictory lives. I wanted to experience the world more than anything and needed to figure out the next stage of my life. He deserved to find someone who could make him happier than I could.

Saleem was shocked and heartbroken. We cried together. I felt sadness, overshadowed by relief.

Dmitri texted me in the middle of Saleem's breakdown, asking if he should reroute his evening flight home through St. Louis. I thought twice about it but told him it wasn't a good time and took it as an opportunity to mention my significant other was moving out.

Saleem was just a memory a few days later.

When Rune arrived back to St. Louis, I was ready. Email contacts had been exported, important documents copied, and personal data deleted from the company server. My performance pay hadn't hit my bank account yet, but I couldn't wait around for that. I knew it would be sacrificed in the end. If there was anything I had learned in the past year, it was that money and things weren't more important than my peace of mind. I'd rather be dirt poor and struggling to follow my dreams than spoiled as a thousand-year-old egg, living a nightmare.

Taking a seat directly across from Rune in the chilly conference room, I took a deep breath. The events of the past year flooded my brain, good times and bad. From our first meet and greet in St. Louis where I ate a medium rare steak to the last supper in Macau when he betrayed me, attempting to exploit me sexually for profit. I thought about it all, the fun, nonsense, challenges, and achievements. The transformation from what I was when I first met Rune to what I had become.

He introduced me to the concept of measuring importance by asking if I would remember a certain event in five or ten years. If not, it didn't matter. This was a simple lesson I have never stopped applying to daily life. Unsure of a path forward, Rune would force me to make a decision and course-correct later.

"Inaction is the worst action," he would say. "You don't need to see the entire staircase to take the first fucking step." He was right. Rune loved to ask me "What's the worst that can happen?" Over time, I would realize that the answer was "not much." Most importantly, he provided me with experiences, and those went far past business know-how.

The role he played in my life was highlighted clear as day. Helping me grow and forcing me to evolve, I was so afraid of the world when I met Rune. Of course, I was intrigued with life beyond the limited confines of my own structured reality, but terror of failure and what-ifs left me paralyzed.

Berating me daily, he shamed it out of me. I often hated him for it, but in the end he broke me of my fear, forcing me to face it, insisting I live past my self-doubt. I finally understood.

Rune taught me not to take life so seriously, to ignore societal norms, and create formidable possibilities for myself. To fail and start over again anew, undeterred. Oddly enough, Rune taught me to enjoy life. And I would be forever grateful. But I had to break free.

Looking him straight in the eye, I dove right in.

"Rune, I want you to know that I appreciate all of the opportunities you've given me, but I think it is time for me to move on from Click!." My voice was calm, yet confident.

That was the absolute last thing he ever expected me to say. Losing his cool, a vivid range of emotions washed over his face. He broke eye contact with me, looking down into his lap for a moment to hide his surprise. Raising his gaze to mine, I could see the slightest hint of sadness in his eyes he fought to hide.

"Why?" he asked, his voice cracking and eyes darting back

and forth.

Rune truly had no idea why I would ever want to leave him and I could never make him understand. In his mind, the cash and material items he threw at me more than made up for his cruel and unusual behavior.

"It's just time for me to move on," I said amicably.

"Bullshit," he spat angrily.

He was a sociopath so I didn't fully understand the presence of his feelings, but I knew they were for me. Our relationship, albeit sick and twisted, was solid. I was Rune's best friend, closer to him than his significant other of a decade. I knew him better than anyone in the world. I practically *was* him. If he lost me, he lost his other half he had meticulously cultivated for the past 465 days.

"How much do you want to stay?" Rune thought he could fix everything with money. "You can just work with Harrison and I'll pay you double," he said with a twinge of desperation.

"It's not about the money, Rune," I said softly.

I couldn't live for Rune forever. I wanted my life back. More importantly, I wanted to create my new life. I was inspired to the max by my time at Click!, from the daily motivation I gained from Rune's self-discipline, to discovering the nomadic adventure lifestyle, and my ultimate return to a creative mindset, picked up from the artists I met along the way. I couldn't stay there.

Rune twiddled a black pen back and forth, a rare sight, as he prided himself on avoiding such tells of anxiety. Ending our conversation abruptly, he stood and stormed out of the conference room, yelling over his shoulder without turning back.

"Sandstone will take care of the paperwork."

Those were the last words Rune would ever speak to me. As fucked up as it may seem, I felt the loss too.

PART III
SATURN RETURN

9 **THE PARTY**

I was free. Free from everything. For the first time in my life, I wasn't playing follow-the-leader. There was just me and I was in harmony with myself, within myself. I tossed my rhinestone stud in the trashcan, sliding a metallic hoop into my nose. A good friend referred me to a new chiropractor to keep me aligned, and I discovered a Thai massage therapist with strong hands just a five-minute walk from my house.

Grabbing coffee with the mentor who connected me to Rune, he strongly advised me not take another job for a few months. His advice freaked me out but I trusted his guidance and agreed to take some time off to focus on myself. It would turn out to be the best decision I ever made, and I'm sure he planned that all along. I wouldn't be surprised if my entire experience with Rune was part of his strategy for me to reach my full potential in life. I couldn't thank him enough.

I had some cash in the bank but not a fortune. While at Click!, I worked constantly, leaving little time to spend money. Traveling on the company's dime the past few months helped as well. I would be good for a while, but not forever. I chose not to worry.

My expenses were minimal, with no cable or car note. I vowed to no longer waste my life watching television, pocketing a measly seven dollars per month canceling Netflix, but more importantly, gaining precious time. I had to give up my Click! phone which meant I now had a cellphone bill, but a friend of mine in the city hooked me up on the low, so I couldn't complain. I didn't care to shop or value material items, so that wasn't an issue. My health and auto insurance remained the same.

Everything else seemed to change.

I took an indefinite break from life and moved at an intentional, present pace. Rising before the sun with a feeling of gratitude, it was a joy to experience yet another day. Each morning a teal and gold kettle-full of savory Super Long Jing green tea sat atop my small wooden tea table, one of few mementos collected during my travels. The tiny Jade teacup burned my fingers. I smiled.

My brassy weighted hula-hoop whipped around my hips to the beat of my favorite music as I watched the sun rise, dying the sky a light pink. Spur of the moment walks to the park on the other side of town turned into entire days spent exploring the cool calmness of the woods.

I used to be the type of person who only displayed and never lit candles, intent on saving them for some unknown special day in the future. Saleem was very keen on burning a rainbow of candles on a large platter in the living room. Over time, the wax melted and a beautiful work of art congealed. After Saleem left, I continued to light the candles daily. When only a trace of the charred black wicks remained, they were replaced with new ones.

Music, smiling, and laughter became my core tools to nurture my jouissance. They were in rotation on the daily, with conscious effort. Evening outings disco dancing in sweaty, crowded hipster basements were good for my soul. Free from worry and caring about what others thought, I sang at the top of my lungs. Little by little, I constructed my daily life and surroundings to my ideal specifications.

Sitting in the sun, drinking green tea and smoking a joint while writing about my travel experiences in kitschy little notebooks, I had never felt better. I loved the details of life and capturing them on thick parchment paper with colorful ink. I didn't want to forget not one.

Even with all of the commotion involved in restructuring and rediscovering my life, Dmitri weighed heavily on my mind. I couldn't get him out of my head. His spirit had painted a phantasmagoria fresco inside my soul, drawing me back to him. It was all-encompassing, seizing my brain. I longed for him.

I couldn't go on one moment longer without telling him exactly how I felt. He was on a weeklong cycling trip and unreachable by phone, so I sat down and composed the first love letter I had ever written.

Hi Dmitri,

How's the trip going? Hope you've got some kick-ass weather; the snow is slowly melting here.

First and foremost, I don't normally write letters like this, but I have a few things to share and I'm a pretty direct person, so here goes:

My life has been composed of a lot of moving parts for a while, but recently increased a bit. I did a lot of thinking during my trip to Panama and decided to leave my position with Click!. It was a difficult decision to make, but ultimately for the best. My boss took the news pretty badly (not speaking to me); however, the end of my personal relationship was a much less chaotic part of the last few weeks.

This brings me to present day. Well, not really. Go back to Panama. From the second I met you, I was immediately drawn to you. I really enjoyed spending time with you, wandering around Casco Viejo, talking, hanging out in your bed . . . I felt so comfortable with you, like I knew you, but I didn't and I still don't. I'm not really sure what to make of that. It was odd but felt very normal at the same time.

This all probably sounds so crazy. I mean, I know it does, because I'm the one typing it and I think it does. I'm just at a point in my life where I don't really care if it sounds crazy, I'm just doing whatever makes me happy. You were the last thing I expected to find in Panama but you just appeared. I looked into your eyes and felt this ridiculous connection and it was amazing. I have never experienced a feeling like that before. I want to feel it again and I want to see you again. Even though I have spent less than like thirty-six hours with you, I feel like this is something worth pursuing. It's crazy.

So, yeah, this email ended up being a little longer and a little more intense than I planned, but oh well. I just wanted to tell you how I felt. Not sure what your feelings are on the situation, what you are looking for, what you aren't looking for, etc. . . .

—Emily

I held my breath until receiving his response a few days later.

Hi Emily,

The trip is going really well. Had a massive ride today up in the hills of Northern California and along the coast. We fly back tomorrow then I'm in Australia for a solid week of work.

So, about everything else. I agree. We had a great connection. It really was like we knew each other from the start. My life also has a lot of moving parts, and I'm not certain how realistic a positive outlook might be on this working given geographic challenges etc. It would be great to connect again soon to see where things go.

Sorry to take so long to get back to you. I've been fairly swamped with sleeping, eating, socializing, riding.

I'm in Utah on the fourteenth. Maybe we can rendezvous somewhere prior to that trip...?

—Dmitri

I was over-the-moon, clutching my chest for fear my heart might detonate into blinding glittery shrapnel of happiness. We made plans to meet at his family's property in Phoenix. A few days after securing our plane tickets, he learned his parents had planned to visit Phoenix the same time. It was decided we would all stay together, as Dmitri traveled extensively for work and didn't get to see his family that often. I was happy to share him and spend more time with Peater and Lillian. They were two of the nicest, most genuine people I had ever met. Plus, spending more time with the parents was a good sign.

Prepping for the trip, I hit the salon for a manicure and

pedicure, stocked up on lingerie in lacy black and satin teal, and made an appointment with my gynecologist to pick up a prescription for birth control. I didn't care how wealthy Dmitri was. A surprise child and baby daddy were nowhere in my master plans. That would seriously cramp my lifestyle.

Nerves took over when my flight was delayed. A conversation with the passenger next to me resulted in a Wedding Singer-type fellowship, with a good portion of the plane engrossed in the saga of my recent life turmoil and pilgrimage to reunite with Dmitri. Wishing me luck as we touched down in Phoenix, thoughts swirled around in my head.

What am I doing here? What if Panama was just a fluke?

Ignoring all the what-ifs, I responded with *why not?*

After exiting the plane I stopped to freshen up. Beautifying myself as much as I could in a foul airport bathroom with dirty countertops and sticky floors, I assessed my appearance. Garbed in a bright pink dress with a high-waist rope belt and tan jacket, on my feet were new sandals I bought just for the trip—brown, silver, and gold. My blown-out shoulder-length hair was freshly colored a glossy reddish purple with my eyes bright and lips shining.

I practiced deep breathing techniques as I walked to the concourse to reunite with Dmitri. They weren't working. My heart was beating out of my chest as I struggled to maintain my composure.

I spotted him immediately. It was as if a large flashing neon arrow was positioned above him, alerting me to his location. There was no turning back. Grinning like a fool, I took a deep breath and marched over without hesitation. He was so unbelievably gorgeous, clad with panache in crisp khaki shorts and dark blue Polo. I watched him search the crowd for me.

"Hey," I said, tapping him on the shoulder. He turned around startled, his eyes sparkling emeralds in my diamond light.

"Hi!" he said in his ever-present adorable accent. "How did you sneak up on me?" he asked. Warmth poured from him. My fears from earlier dispelled within less than a millisecond. I was complete at his side.

"Hi," I said again. "No idea," I lost myself in his eyes, desire building already. He stared into me with the same intensity. It was a familiar scene, Dmitri and I floating in a time warp of adulation, blinded to the rest of the world.

Outstretching his arm, he held a white coffee cup and smiled enchantingly. "For you."

In a trance, it took me a few moments to realize he was handing me a latte.

"Oh, thank you so much," I said, grabbing the warm cup as I blushed slightly, bashfully turning away to regain my poise.

The energy surrounding him was insane. When ours combined, we created a cyclonic effect sealing the two of us off into our own world. Everything else was just white noise.

Dmitri loaded my luggage in to the car and drove to Old Scottsdale for dinner with his parents. He ordered wine, remembering I liked white as he chose a robust red for himself, and we took seats at the bar. I couldn't stop smiling. I had returned to my version of heaven on Earth, which was Dmitri's energy field. It fit so perfectly with mine.

"Hey there, Smiley!" Peater called out as he and Lillian approached the bar. I continued to beam, happy as happy could be.

"Hello, how are you?" We greeted each other with hugs and were seated at a snug corner table. Indulging in an informal dinner, the Aussies and I engaged in thought-provoking conversation that encompassed everything you should never discuss: politics, religion, guns, even abortion.

The galleries were closed by the time our late-night supper ended so we strolled around Old Scottsdale window-viewing art after hours from the empty sidewalk. The desert sky clear and stars bright, the banter between the four of us humorous and pleasant.

Later that evening we stepped into a Norman Rockwell painting, lazing next to the fire pit on the patio, sipping wine and giggling. Peater, Dmitri, and Lillian were enjoying the

Tupperware full of homemade chocolate chip cookies I gifted them. Baked in my kitchen in St. Louis, they had traveled 1,500 miles to their destination.

Cookies could be considered my personal version of guanxi. Also, I just like to make others feel happy. However, I didn't really need much grease on the wheels here. Peater and Lillian seemed to genuinely enjoy my company.

"Emily, have I told you the story about the time Peater bought three houses in one weekend?" Lillian said to me.

"What? No," I responded, laughing.

"Okay, okay," Peater chimed in, waving his arms in an exaggerated manner. "I think the story is being taken a bit out of context here," he said with a big grin. "It was one of my first trips to Scottsdale and I happened upon a house I really liked, so I put a deposit on it. Then I saw another one I really liked right after it, and it was a great deal so I got that one, too."

"Who needs two houses in Scottsdale?!" Lillian interjected with a hoot. "Plus Peater, then you did it *again*," she wagged her finger at him playfully.

"Yes, I did. After the second house, I found a third one. That is true." Looking for camaraderie, he turned to me and said, "Emily, the houses were *only one hundred thousand dollars* each. They were a steal." Speaking authentically from his life perspective, he was being honest. Peater and Lillian could never be the least bit pretentious. They were kind, generous, loving people.

To them, in their reality, $100,000 was a steal, and clearly involved zero risk on their behalf. It was, however, a statement that would be incredulous to someone from middle class America. Most people I knew would work their entire lives in an attempt to pay off one single $100,000 mortgage, if they managed to be approved for a loan.

Dmitri's family and I lived in different universes—that was crystal clear to me at this point. They didn't seem to get it yet. I thought I'd help them understand.

"Wow, you should start investing in property in St. Louis.

My house cost thirty-five thousand dollars," I deadpanned. The conversation fell momentarily silent, as they processed the yin shock I provided in response to their yang. I wasn't ashamed of my background or status in the world. My possessions and imaginary class level didn't define me. I was committed to being my 100 percent authentic self.

"Really?" Peater asked, perplexed.

"Yep. I took advantage of the US housing crisis and snagged an eighty-eight-year-old foreclosed home in the neighborhood where I grew up, about twenty minutes north of St. Louis City."

"So you live in a suburb outside of the city?" Lillian asked, curious.

"Yes." I continued. "It's not a huge house, just a smaller two-bedroom bungalow. It's actually more space than I need. The previous owners left it in good shape. I've just been updating it here and there as I'd like." I paused, assessing the temperature of the conversation. They seemed interested. "I just put down new flooring throughout the house, bought new kitchen appliances, and I'm in the middle of updating the bathroom right now. My grandmother lives right down the street from me so that was really helpful while the shower was being retiled. I would just run over to her house and shower during that process."

"Why didn't you just use another bathroom?" Dmitri asked, confused.

"My house only has one bathroom," I explained, smiling. The expression on his face was priceless. I could tell he had never lived in a house with just one bathroom. The subtle differences in people's lives are astonishing. "I'm actually really glad I only have one bathroom, because I've discovered I do not enjoy painting bathrooms," I chuckled.

"Wait. You're painting your bathroom *yourself?*" Lillian asked, incredulous yet completely sincere.

"Yes. I paint everything myself. And do most of the work myself. Well, my family helps me, but I don't hire contractors. My family really enjoys home renovation. They've always done all of the work on their houses themselves and have also flipped a house or two." Their jaws hung open, stunned.

"Wow. Well, aren't you an interesting one!" Peater's eyes lit up like his sons as he patted me on the back. They were shocked, and most likely inferring what they felt those statements meant about the rest of my life, background, and social status—all of those meaningless things. I could tell Peater liked my scrappy personality. He and Lillian had no judgment for me, only innocuous inquisitiveness. I'm not sure I can say the same for Dmitri.

As the late evening turned to early morning, Dmitri and I shared longing glances in anticipation of being alone. After what felt like years, we finally retreated to our shared room, hand-in-hand, holding back our excitement with pursed lips. His parents' room was just down the hall from us.

Both tired from a long day of travel and wine, we watched each other undress in silence and slipped into bed. Dmitri wrapped his strong arms around me where they belonged, sighing in contentment and bringing his lips to mine. I smiled like crazy, unable to properly return his kiss. He pulled back and connected to my gaze, tracing his finger over my collarbone.

"You are so beautiful. It feels good to be next to you again." His voice was strong and feelings clear.

"You too. I love the way I feel when I'm with you," I confessed, sinking into him and allowing the weight of his body to wash over me. Any other feeling in life was a waste of time.

He pulled the sheets over our heads and kissed my neck. Morphine pumped through my veins and I floated from my body, resting comfortably on a heap of bliss. We tried to be quiet.

Our days in Phoenix stretched like warm taffy. Dmitri would awaken before sunrise each morning, gently kissing me to consciousness so we could revel in each other in the privacy of the slumbering world. Conspicuously relaxed and flushed in happiness, we joined his parents for breakfast together on the patio in their perfectly manicured Scottsdale backyard. It was professionally landscaped, of course.

Breakfast consisted of dainty little jams and preservatives, whole-wheat oatmeal, trays of sliced organic fruit, selections of toast and biscuits, a few crepe-like pancakes Dmitri's mother prepared from scratch, orange juice, green tea for me, coffee, and milk. It was picturesque. Their entire lives were. Our breakfast discussion was as pleasant as the perfect climate we experienced, lounging under the cool morning sun.

Dmitri and I grabbed coffee on the way to hike Pinnacle Peak. He picked up an Eric Clapton CD with our drinks, and we sang the songs together in the white rental car as we puttered down the flat, dusty Arizona streets. He wouldn't let me help him with the GPS even though he had his hands full driving and wasn't the best multitasker. We made it eventually.

Pointing out a fancy BMW SUV in the parking lot he said, "That's the kind of car I drive."

I nodded in the direction of an older Honda Civic and countered, "That's the kind of car I drive."

Hiking to the peak, Dmitri told me about his recently acquired hobby of collecting musical memorabilia. Each piece on his want list was priced higher than my entire college education.

"Yeah, I kind of stopped buying material items about a year ago. I prefer experiences," I said.

"Huh." He squinted his eyes and smiled at me. "You little hipster," he teased, grabbing my waist and kissing me. Our lives were not necessarily parallels. That didn't matter. My eyes adored every bit of Dmitri exactly as he was. His mind was incredibly complex. I had immense respect for him. He was naturally dominant, exuding confidence at all times, and devastatingly gorgeous. I wanted him naked again.

After our hike, Dmitri proposed cooling down with a "crisp glass of white wine." Driving to a high-end shopping plaza, we settled in at Tommy Bahama's for drinks and appetizers. Sitting at the bar was an older lady with a frozen, expressionless face who had obviously spent way too much money on plastic surgery. Next to her was a fancy baby stroller with two miniature Chihuahuas inside, dressed in pink. She was feeding them lobster. This didn't seem to faze my companion.

We drank and talked for a few hours, gazing into each other's eyes. Dmitri was smarter, quicker, more determined, and more successful than me. He asked questions I had never thought about and didn't know the answers to, which was an odd feeling, but only increased my admiration for him.

After a while shopping commenced, first a schmoozy jewelry store so Dmitri could have his watch loosened to adjust to the climate difference from his recent business trip in Russia. Next was a shoe boutique where he tried on three pairs of almost-identical hiking boots, asking my opinion while I stood on feigning interest.

Pushing me into girly stores, I could tell Dmitri wanted to buy me things. However, I didn't want anything, I only wanted to learn more about him and look into his eyes. I became very aware of the fact that our love languages were somewhat misaligned. Material items did not mean much to me, yet I could tell that an important aspect of Dmitri's identity was his resources, and spending money was a large part of the way he showed affection.

After repeatedly refusing his offers to purchase things for me I had no desire to possess, he seemed to give up. We then popped into a music memorabilia shop where he debated whether or not to add a framed Rolling Stones piece to his collection.

Breaking for more wine and lunch on the patio of a lovely little cafe, Dmitri opened up about his past. This was what I desired. Openness and vulnerability, not money or things.

Computer science was an innate talent, breezing through his classes at Harvard and creating what he described as a social media network similar to Facebook, long before Zuckerberg would ever set foot on campus at Dmitri's alma mater. He presented it to his father as an organizational tool for the family company. His face fell to sadness and a slight hint of resentment as he recounted how his father ignored what he knew to be an innovative, game-changing contribution. His project was effectively shut down. I could feel the disappointment he wouldn't allow to show. I felt honored he let me near it at all.

After all those years, now a respected, accomplished businessman, he still carried around on his fancy AirMac the code for that antiquated program he put so much of himself into so long ago. It was an important event in his life and seemed to manifest into a quest for his father's approval that had yet to cease. I squeezed his hand, willing to take on his pain and offer my positive energy and love in return. I recognized his heart in mine. He smiled at me as we sat in the sun, our fingers entangled, mirroring our souls.

Late afternoon we were to meet Peater and Lillian for drinks before dinner. Dmitri, being the incredibly thoughtful person that he was, arranged quite the evening.

"Emily," he said suddenly, a light bulb popping up over his head.

"Yes, Dmitri," I smiled serenely.

"I know the perfect place for drinks. One of my favorite restaurants has an outdoor patio with a view of the sunset that is almost as beautiful as you."

He knew exactly the right things to say. Every syllable pulled me in deeper but I was already past the point of no return.

"I'll make reservations for the four of us," he said decisively.

I loved not having to make decisions all the time. It was so nice to be in the presence of a real man.

Our outing was, as expected, enchanting. Peater, Lillian, Dmitri, and I were confirmed a natural fit. Clutching glasses of fine vino, we noshed on pasta noodles using understated matte silverware. The tone of our conversation was lighthearted and upbeat, meandering through subterranean and surface topics, jumping from wine diapers to the recent US election, seguing into an assessment of racial tensions in the States, followed by a discussion about my nail polish, which I always chose by the name of the color. That day I was wearing *Vampsterdam,* a mysterious plum.

I watched as Peater reappraised me, yet again impressed by how smart and diverse I was. Those who are meant to, eventually come to realize the error of their preconceptions. We relished the night, trading merriment without a care in the world. It was a marvelous life.

"Don't you just love dining, Emily?" Peater asked me with a brilliant smile full of joy.

"I do," I returned his smile, upping it by a few watts.

Dmitri's family knew how to live. I decided to follow their example and stream through life effortlessly as a zephyr. No, I didn't have millions of dollars, but I wouldn't let that stop me from attaining their level of happiness and fulfillment. No worries. I'd figure it out.

After dinner, Dmitri insisted we grab frozen yogurt and a bottle of wine and head back to the house to watch a movie. "I know you don't necessarily like to go out all the time. I remember you told me you can be a hermit. Why don't we just stay in tonight?" he asked.

His consideration melted my heart. I would have been thrilled doing anything Dmitri wanted to do. But he wanted to do what *I* wanted to do. He gave me a feeling unlike any other.

Returning to the house, we set up a fort on the couch, both squeezing onto one cushion together. Unable to pull up his favorite movie on iTunes, we substituted with the runner-up, one I had never seen nor heard of, which was rare. Dmitri was an absolutely perfect complement to me.

Lightly running my fingers up and down his arm in gentle affection, he began to snore halfway through the movie. I didn't mind. I took it as an opportunity to memorize his features, the lines in his face, curves of his lips, texture of his hair, the way his chest contracted and fell with each breath.

The next morning we repeated our Saturday Evening Post cover scene from the day before. I sat happily in the sun, barefoot and sipping green tea as I smeared dark purple organic jam onto a slice of golden toasted wheat bread. Peater and I were attempting to identify a bird that had decided to join us on the patio for breakfast. He was a birder and had strategically placed a birdhouse in the yard to attract beautiful creatures to study.

After breakfast, Peater and Lillian trotted off to flying lessons. Dmitri and I sat in the kitchen, contemplating our plans for the day.

"I know you've never been to the Grand Canyon. We can hire a helicopter pilot to take us around. How does that sound?"

That sounded unnecessarily expensive and not very conducive to conversation.

"Hmm. True, I have not been to the Grand Canyon. What are our other possibilities?"

"Well . . . I'm having a mid-life or quarter-life crisis or something lately. I've been spending a lot of money. Like *a lot* of money," his eyes widened as he looked at me in exaggeration.

I had no idea what Dmitri considered *a lot* of money, but I'm sure as hell it was at least ten billion times more than I considered *a lot* of money. I literally couldn't process it.

"But lately I've been wanting to buy a vintage Porsche convertible. . . . I guess we could go find one if you want," he shrugged nonchalantly.

I was incapable of being flabbergasted. Luckily, I had spent time with extremely wealthy and powerful people over the past year, gradually becoming accustomed to the lifestyles of those who knew no worries. It was at first a distant, incomprehensible existence, but one that piqued my curiosity. Over time, I became capable of traversing the upper crust as if I was born into it—when I wanted to. Without those experiences, I would have been completely weirded out by Dmitri and his family. I was no fish out of water. However, I was at the time oblivious to the fact that I was a fish on a bicycle.

I wanted to know more about Dmitri, learn his passions

and desires, understand the way his brain worked.

"You know, it doesn't really matter to me. You're more familiar with the area. Let's do something you enjoy. I just want to spend some time with you and get to know you better. What do you like to do?" I asked.

My response seemed to be novel to him. His indigo eyes glistened and shot an electric current through me, his smile a match setting my soul ablaze as if it had been doused in kerosene.

"Well, there's the Frank Lloyd Wright museum. I really love architecture and I haven't been. We could go there," he said after some thought.

I beamed. "Sounds perfect. We can check out some vintage car auctions afterwards."

It was a great idea. The desert vibes were high and smooth. We wandered around the bookstore at Taliesin West with our hands clasped together. Watching as Dmitri fell into the pages of a book titled *Houses Made of Wood and Light*, I could tell it resonated with him.

He spoke with conviction, the words flowing from him. "Emily, if I could be anything, I would be an architect. I want to build boats."

Dmitri possessed superior intelligence and was obviously successful in his career. But it was strikingly apparent that it wasn't his chosen passion. I took note of the name of the book as we left, already plotting to surprise Dmitri with inspiration after he returned to Australia. If anybody had the means to pursue what they loved, it was him.

We met his parents at the house and cleaned up from our rough day of perusing museums and searching for vintage sports cars. I emerged in an emerald blue dress, gold Coach wedges, and shiny tresses. My gold 'E' ring encircled my finger as it did every day, neck adorned with a sparkly crystal that found me in Boulder, Colorado a year prior.

"Look at you!" Peater exclaimed, as I entered the living room. I smiled, blushing. He certainly approved.

Dmitri poked his head in from the hallway, his eyes

softening and mouth turning into a grin.

"Holy shit," he said, under his breath.

His strong arms wrapped around my waist from behind, the warmth of his body enveloping mine. A shiver went down my back as he gently placed a kiss on my neck. My panties were wet and his dad was in the room. Awkward. Sharing a knowing look accompanied by an electric spark, he then glanced down toward his pants and laughed. We retreated to separate ends of the room in order to return to a reasonable state of mind, at least until his parents left.

Dmitri's friends from summers spent in Phoenix, Clay and Teresa, were to be our pre-dinner drink dates that evening. They stormed in, a tornado of hospitality and barrel of laughs. I absolutely loved them and the feeling was mutual. We connected instantly.

Piling into Clay's tiny two-door BMW sports car, Dmitri escorted me to the front seat, of course, as he squeezed in the back. We met up with Dmitri's parents and more friends for dinner. Dining on the second-floor open-air patio, a slight breeze enhanced the bone-dry temperature in perfect harmony. Aged wine flowed freely and the cuisine was scrumptious, our meal topped off with perfectly scorched vanilla crème brûlée.

Eager to exhibit my diversity, Peater invited me to join discussions geared toward my expansive wheelhouse. Turning it on, my infectious humor, unusual intellect, and trillion-dollar smile dazzled every last one in the group. Dmitri locked eyes with me and lusted.

I never wanted it to end, with him right across from me, smiling into my eyes over the flickering candlelight. I knew I could do this for life. I could play the role. I could be her. I *wanted* to be her, as long as I could be with him. It would be worth it. I would never need anything more, if only I could be with him. He was all I ever wanted.

As our last night together in Phoenix and with such good company, Dmitri and I had quite a few toasts, imbibing in more wine than planned. I distractedly clinked my glass with his while daydreaming off into the distance.

"Emily, you should always look people in the eyes when you're toasting," he said while looking into mine.

I listened. I listened to every single thing Dmitri ever said to me as if it were the only thing I had ever heard. In a certain aspect, it was. I readily surrendered to his energy, accepting all of his knowledge, instinctively trusting him.

Clay and his wife dropped us off at the house, hugging goodbye, drunkenly cracking up over an earlier hilarious incident that has since faded into obscurity within my memory. We went straight to the bedroom. Dmitri shut and locked the door. He stared at me with hunger in his bloodshot eyes. They were more beautiful than ever, the red contrast causing the vibrant blue to intensify. I stared back at him seductively, pulling my dress over my head and dropping it on the floor, revealing black lingerie.

He breathed heavily, fumbling with the buttons on his shirt. "Oh my God, you are so fucking gorgeous."

"*You* are so fucking gorgeous. Take your clothes off," I responded with earnest.

I just wanted him next to me, on top of me, inside of me, his mouth covering mine, and hands on my bare skin. I didn't know when I would see him again after Phoenix. I had to take in as much of him as I could. We were not successful in being quiet.

Dmitri's iPhone beeped at 6:00 am. He managed to remember to set his alarm in our drunken haze. I was impressed. This would be our last time alone before I got on a plane back to St. Louis. It was much different from the night before.

Faint light from the morning sun cast over our exposed skin, chests pressed together, warm mouths kissing slowly, deeply. Dmitri ran his fingers over my lips, tenderly kissing my forehead, praising me for my beauty, speaking in awe of it. His inescapable gaze illuminated parts of my being I didn't know existed until that very moment.

No one could ever look at me the way Dmitri did. His mere presence compelled me to submit to him without hesitation.

The feeling was unlike anything human beings had previously been capable of eliciting from me. It was simply indescribable. The meaning of life, or mine, at least.

If the Phoenix trip had been some type of audition, I nailed that shit. Smiling and hugging Peater and Lillian goodbye, I was confident we would see each other again. Loading my luggage into the car, they invited me to their cabin at the lake that summer. They were delightful.

Dmitri drove to the airport with his palm clasped over mine, wistfully kissing the back of my hand every so often. I couldn't take my eyes off of him.

Delayed by a long security line, Dmitri's flight was boarding when we reached his gate. A private symphony filled our ears. Staring into each other's eyes, we said nothing, unsure of what life was for us now. A final boarding call for his plane echoed over the loudspeaker.

"We'll figure out our next move via email," he asserted, grabbing his briefcase.

I nodded, my chest tightening. I didn't want him to leave.

"I'll miss you, Jude," he said slowly, taken to referring to me by my tattoo.

Every word we ever wanted to say to each other poured from our eyes.

"You too," I said with a bittersweet smile, kissing him on the cheek.

We would meet again, when kismet allowed.

10 JUST DO IT

Back in St. Louis, I was excited to live my life. Tired of making other people's dreams come true at the expense of my own, it was time to believe in myself. I would create. Energy and inspiration flowed through me freely. Everything was magical. Opportunities abounded. I just had to set forth intent.

There is no spoon.

I went full speed ahead to realizing my passion and purpose in life. What was the worst that could happen? Trying and failing? Ending up broke? Resorting to a mindless, repetitive office job? Been there, done that. No fear remained within me. Worrying accomplished absolutely nothing. It didn't exist in my world any longer. I simply stopped doing it.

No longer making huge life decisions out of fear of the unknown, I forged ahead as a writer, my true passion. The past year of my life had given me a story – the ultimate story. I couldn't ignore it.

Maintaining a smile was a conscious decision. There have been countless instances in my life when amazing things have taken shape that can be traced back to an interaction that wouldn't have happened if I had a scowl to offer instead of a smile.

Laughter remained the Philips screwdriver of my happiness

toolbox. Refusing to create negative energy through anger, resentment, stress, worry or regret, I chose to laugh instead. The option of frowning and cursing the world when I spilled a latte on my shirt always existed, but I laughed and smiled, truly grateful knowing the accident could have only occurred had I lived in a country economically well-off enough for me to accumulate the cash to be able to buy $6 USD coffee in the first place.

Skydiving had been on my bucket list for ten years but no one would ever go with me. I woke up one morning and decided I had waited long enough. Smoking a joint and singing along to Sergeant Pepper's Lonely Hearts Club Band, I drove two hours into rural Missouri at 7:00 am. The skydiving instructors were taken aback that I was alone. I shrugged.

Throwing myself out of an airplane was an experience like none other. In that moment, I embodied in physical form the obscene sense of freedom my spirit had already achieved. The plane and parachute were simply tools to aid in my expression. I jumped twice within a few days, the second time floating down-to-earth through thick cotton-candy clouds, white and fluffy. Sending Dmitri a selfie from the prop plane at 10,000 feet, he was terrified.

Tying a perfect electric-blue ribbon bow on chartreuse paper impeccably wrapped around a copy of the book Dmitri so coveted at the architecture museum in Phoenix, I shipped off my special international cargo. The inscription was hardly indiscriminate. After careful thought, a sentiment conveyed through lyrics written by Mick Jagger was the right decision. I lovingly penned it in elegant script on the inside cover. It would be there forever.

Reaching out to my network, I scheduled a slew of coffees, lunches, and drinks. Never satiated doing just one thing at a time, a brainstorming session with a mentor and friend led me to meticulously research and plan a week-long nature festival celebrating migratory birds and directly benefiting the City of St. Louis for years to come.

I created a spectacular event proposal that clearly outlined its link to regional economic prosperity by way of wealthy, educated, well-traveled birders. The confluence of the Missouri and Mississippi River near St. Louis attracted over sixty percent of North American birds each year. It was a no-brainer.

Navigating through my connections, I arranged a meeting with city officials and a few influential birding and nature organizations to present my proposal. Dmitri was available to meet the same week. Sharing my economic development endeavors with him, I didn't hesitate to reschedule our rendezvous in order to prepare for my presentation, although he had a very busy few months coming up with work and travel. It was an important meeting for me.

The birding proposal was well-received. All in attendance agreed that the plan was air-tight, profitable outcome a sure bet, and viewed the increased public awareness and support of conservation as a reinforcement of the region's commitment to preservation of nature. Then the other shoe dropped.

I was informed that the individual birding organizations in the area didn't play well together and would require too much work to create a cooperative event. The plan was scrapped. Hundreds of hours of my time were tossed into the recycling bin in front of my eyes.

I rebounded with ease. Birding wasn't my passion; it had just been one opportunity where I could put my magic bag of skills to use. I kept my ear to the ground for my next move, maintaining a strict foundation of laughing, smiling, dancing, and positivity.

Dmitri sent me a close-up from a Rolling Stones concert attended during a business trip to London. Mick Jagger had just sung the lyrics from his inscription a few feet in front of him. "Lose your dreams and you might lose your mind." Dmitri was having the time of his life. I was happy he was happy.

At the last-minute, I learned of an event in Brooklyn honoring my favorite musician and activist, Adam Yauch, AKA MCA from the Beastie Boys. Scheduled for that upcoming weekend, it was in an area Harrison was familiar with. I emailed him and mentioned I was thinking about attending but wasn't sure, considering the late notice and distance from St. Louis.

His response was short and perfect.

Do it.

Harrison was wise and it would behoove me to ignore his advice. I booked my flight for the two-day trip immediately after our conversation. A family vacation to Manhattan when I was seventeen was the only experience I had with New York other than layovers at the airport. Dmitri and I planned to meet in New York for the weekend but our hopes were thwarted by his required presence at a one-percenters' investment conference attended by the likes of Warren Buffett. I can't make this stuff up.

Hopping on a plane, I landed at John F. Kennedy International Airport and Googled subway directions to Classon Avenue. I was staying in a shared living space in Clinton Hill, Brooklyn. Checking into apartment 113, I was given a key and directed to a private queen bed dedicated just for me. Private beds are something I will never take for granted again after Panamocalypse.

The morning of MCA Day was warm and sticky. Sipping coffee while sweating in jean shorts, a cream tank top and bamboo high tops with a neon green swoosh, I made my way to Littlefield, an independent art space where the event would be held. The infamous Beastie Caddy decked-out in graffiti marked the spot, gleaming in the sun. Beastie vinyl spun on the turntables, Beastie art covered the walls, and Beastie videos played nonstop while breakdancers as young as five spun around on the stage.

The positivity and goodwill was overwhelming in the best sense. I had found my people, bonding over our love for classic jams, values of old school hip-hop culture, and of course, Beastie evangelical inclusiveness and ludicrousness. I had no idea there were so many others. Warm, welcoming, and unique yet like-minded individuals of all walks of life gathered in one place, sharing stories of growing up with the Beasties, grieving the loss of Yauch, celebrating his courageous contributions to the world, and making new memories with old friends we didn't know we had.

The sense of community energized me. I felt the love and knew it was something I needed to be a part of. Reaching out to the MCA Day organizers, I let them know they could count on me for anything and everything during planning for next year's event.

On my last day in New York, I burst awake full of life before sunrise. Securing my backpack, I scrawled a note of thanks and left it on the table with the apartment key, heading out into the Big Apple. The deserted early morning streets were quiet and peaceful, some alleys Wild-Style graffitied with animated 3D tags. I moseyed along enjoying the bright silence for a few hours. Stumbling upon the Brooklyn Bridge, it only made sense to cross it, continuing on my self-guided walking tour of NYC.

The pedestrian traffic on the bridge was chaotic. Bikers rang their bells furiously as photo-snapping tourists blocked their exercise routes. Kids begged their parents for frozen lemonade from vendors strategically located smack-dab in the middle of the sweltering mile-long trek. Women clicked their way from one end to another in red-bottomed stilettos, which puzzled and impressed me. I had no idea how they did it and no intention of finding out for myself. My green high tops were stylish enough.

I snapped a picture of the skyline and East River for Dmitri. He said New York was his favorite city. Dumping me into Manhattan at the end of the line, I continued my urban exploration for hours.

Steering clear of the Times Square tourist trap, it was my mission to find parts of the city people rarely think about and never visit. I marched along dingy buildings and gleaming skyscrapers, snacking on dumplings dripping dark soy sauce while perusing kitschy paintings, capturing photos of enough street art to fill my own gallery, and burning the roof of my mouth with slices of pizza purchased from hole-in-the-wall pizzerias. The unforgiving sun beat down, drenching me in sweat as I toted my backpack around the city for hours amid white-hot temperatures.

Catching some shade beneath a willowy tree in Central Park en route to the airport, I was approached by a monk. We stood in silence as he grasped my hands in prayer for a few moments before slipping a talisman around my wrist, leaving me with the words "lifetime peace." I didn't know why he chose me but it made me smile.

Ever grateful to Harrison for his prized life advice, New York had been a soul-inspiring trip full of creativity, watering the planted seeds in my mind.

11 HOPEFULLY SUCCINCT

I t's so good to hear your voice, Jude," Dmitri said.

Our phone conversations were sporadic but heavy, the distance forcing us to fast-forward the development of our relationship. Values, career choices, family, children, goals, roles, plans, needs. I just wanted him.

All of our attempts to rendezvous never panned out. He had a billion things going on as VP of a huge company, with his schedule set months in advance by an assistant. I had a million things going on constructing a new life, my schedule set each moment by me. It didn't matter. I was ready to take a leap of faith and move 10,000 miles across the planet to Australia as soon as he said the word. My priority was to be happy. Dmitri made me happier than anything.

I knew changing our entire lives based upon a not-so-fluke meeting of two people on a water taxi in Panama was a quixotic, starry-eyed move. But crazier things had happened. Everything single thing about Dmitri and I thus far had been out of a fairy tale. Why not this? I was willing to sacrifice everything and go all in if he was.

I refused to waste one more second when I knew the possibility of love that was out there for me. I knew firsthand how quickly people and feelings can fade into the background. It was now or never.

Laying myself at the feet of another, I poured the hidden corners of my heart into the second love letter I have ever written, what I knew would be the final letter, one way or the other. It was a risk I had no choice but to take. Fate can only get you so far. Once you're there, it's up to you to make it happen.

Hi Dmitri,

This email may seem very forward. I'm okay with that. Dependent upon how you feel, it could be one of the coolest letters you get or one of the craziest. Regardless, it will likely be one of the most honest.

I'm not used to pursuing men (especially not in a different country), therefore, I have no clue whether or not this is appropriate, or too much, or what. However, for me, any potential embarrassment or rejection pales in comparison to ambiguity or regret regarding matters of the heart. Warning: This will probably read like a Nicholas Sparks novel.

I'm very clear about how I feel about you.

I know you don't know me that well, and I was in the tail-end of a relationship when you met me, but I don't come across people that I connect with often. Very rarely. I've met all kinds of men from around the world, all ages, professions, personalities. They're okay. But I've never in my life met anyone that makes me feel the way you do.

I haven't seen you in a few months, but I think about you and your blue eyes all the time. I'm attracted to the way your mind works, your passion for life, adventure and family. Your intelligence, drive, humor, and good heart. I didn't know any of those things about you when I first met you, but honestly, you had me from hello. That is probably the simplest way to put it.

I only live once and I know what I want. Ultimately, I want a partner with shared values that I can connect with, can't keep my hands off of, and is just as multifaceted, passionate, adventurous, and awesome as I am. I see that in you and I would be stupid to ignore it. If you see that in me, I'm willing to make that happen. Whether that is meeting in Chicago, St. Louis, Australia, Argentina . . . or whatever that entails. I can do whatever I want with my life, and I do. It's pretty awesome. The only way it could be any better is if I could share some of those experiences with you.

I know that we both felt a connection in Panama, or we wouldn't have met in Arizona. Although it's kind of heavy, I needed to take the risk and tell you how I feel so I had no regrets.

If you share my feelings and see the possibility of that with me—fantastic. If you don't—that's cool, too. It's just, at this point, I have real feelings for you and need to know what to do with them. . . .

—Emily

A few minutes after I hit send, I received a text from him saying that he was in the middle of a hectic work trip but received my email and would respond soon.

I didn't hear from Dmitri for days. It felt like decades. Time rots even the heartwood of a cedar. When he finally replied, his words were brief:

Hey Jude,

You are beautiful. You are an absolutely amazing person and I've never met anyone like you. I have strong feelings for you and know there is a connection between us. But it would take years for us to begin to understand each other. I think you are seeking more from life than I am. We as Australians only feel the need to affect our immediate surroundings, we don't desire more than that. I think you are brilliant. And you will be recognized for that. But I don't see my partner as aggressively ambitious as you.

Hopefully succinct.

And a few moments later:

I liked your letter.

That was that. It could have been, but it was not. Dmitri disappeared from my life as casually as he breezed in.

A fistful of love sucker-punched me in the nose, leaving my eyes burning and pride tattered. It hit me hard. Harder than I would have liked and much harder than I care to admit. I had no air to breathe. I was unable to move, staring into the distance, shell-shocked. The colors of the world faded to grayscale, my struggling heartbeat drowning out any hopes of sweet sounds.

Lost in my mind, I questioned everything about myself and my life. The universe was flipped upside down and inside out. Nothing made sense. Losing the possibility of that happiness was one thing. The crime of being too ambitious blindsided me. It struck an echoing chord deep inside of my being. That *was* me.

I'd be lying if I said I didn't think ambitious was a bit sugarcoated and could have been replaced with low class, but pretended not to see it, choosing to deal with the surface issue alone. The rest was too much. Too painful to consider.

My heart raced and blood pumped faster and faster until I could no longer sit still. I flicked a green lighter and took a drag of a cigarette, allowing myself to feel the pain as I exhaled. Masking my heartbreak in the pitch-black night, a stream of tears to rival the Muddy Mississippi poured down my face, mixing with salty sweat from the thick August heat. My eyes once full of enigmatic light now sat as empty deserted vessels echoing bittersweet memories of the past.

The reality of a lifetime without Dmitri's warmth was devastating. I would never again feel his gaze upon me or the light of his love within me. Ragged breath heaved in and out, catching in my throat and choking me as I clutched my chest and went through it. I just wanted to love him. Tossed to the side and cracked, my soul wavered.

It took every bit of strength within me to acknowledge and discard the love I had for Dmitri. Gutting my engorged heart, a tourniquet was not the solution. I had to let it bleed. Let it out and let it in.

And then it was time to let it go. If I had learned anything from past relationships, it was to accept the end and move on. Shit happens, people make their choices, and there is no right or wrong. Life goes on.

It would have gone on whether I wrote that letter or not. At least now I knew. It's always better to know.

I could only be me and my undeniable destiny for greatness had already bested my happily ever after. If I couldn't have Dmitri because of my ambition, I damned well better do something motherfucking spectacular with it.

But I would never forget the feeling we found at the edge of the Caribbean Sea. And it would be blasphemous to accept anything less than what the universe had shown me was possible. I sought only the most divine of connections, one that made my heart sing and nothing less—and knew there was a chance it would never be found.

I had to be ok with that.

12 HIGH PLAINS DRIFTER

Actively battling my lifelong programming to stress out and take the next minimum wage job for a 'stable paycheck,' I moved toward my dreams. Motivation came by way of fearless friends who were out in the world at that very moment, living their passions. Adventuring, experiencing, and using their imaginations, they rejected society's definition of their purpose, instead conjuring one of their own.

Fed up with Rune's bullshit, Harrison resigned from Click! and vanished to his bat cave. Sandstone decided to jump ship as well, shopping scholarships to grad schools. Reid parted ways with Click! shortly thereafter, capitalizing on new industry connections to build his own film company.

Gabe dangled over thundering waterfalls in the jungles of the Amazon to capture shots from death-defying perspectives. Felix was winning photography awards back-to-back for his skiing chronicles. Benjamin roamed around third-world villages in Southeast Asia while Lazar conquered the North Pole and Luca continued to spend his days in the solitude of Mother Nature. They gave my belief of a cool, creative future a shot in the arm.

I was confident that the world would work with

me in tandem to keep everything running smoothly while I built a fantastic life. Snubbing worries, I chipped away at my book, writing every day. I would live just fine until I figured out what was next.

Gary, who helped me with Rune's wedding, proposed partnering to create a Panama travel company. It was an open market, we had the connections, overhead costs would be minimal, and any potential of getting paid to travel was an automatic yes.

Holding Skype meetings at odd hours we went to work. I was an entrepreneur and I liked it, tackling each day with a sense of purpose and satisfaction.

It wasn't all rainbow skrink-la-doos and sugar-encrusted snozzberries. It was a solitary life, one that required holding the deepest belief in myself and my purpose in order not to crack under the pressure and isolation. Your life is seen only by yourself and the universe, therefore it doesn't exist outside of your own mind until manifested into tangible reality.

My struggle was a chosen one. I would never be a slave to someone else again, grinding day and night to accomplish *their* goals. I hadn't given a fair effort to make my own dreams materialize.

It was not a crisis or a phase. This was a lifestyle change. Ignoring the cheese of mass consumption, I managed to tunnel my way out of the rat race, never to return again. I refused to settle and wouldn't stop chasing my dreams until I was living them. I felt the same way about my love life, which was almost harder for people to accept.

A single, twenty-nine-year-old female with no feasible prospects for a husband was the end of the world to most. Worse than not having a stable job, was not having a man. Any man. Even Sandstone jumped on the bandwagon.

"You're twenty-nine and broke up with your boyfriend? Geesh, Emily. At least you have good bone structure. Best of luck with that."

Although it would be nice to be in love, I did not fear being alone. I would never sacrifice myself for security again.

I didn't need Rune telling me what to do in order to be successful. I didn't need Dmitri to love me for me to keep loving life. I didn't need to wait for someone to accompany me on my adventures or approve of my plans. All I needed was me.

I moved full speed ahead with the travel company, planning my first solo international trip. Remembering that everyone was my peer, I reached out to the top businesses around the Republic of Panama, scheduling tours of private islands, visits to super-exclusive resorts, and gourmet meals at trendy restaurants.

I would travel to Casco Viejo, Bocas del Toro, Panama City, Portobelo, Buenaventura, and Playa Bonita, visiting more of the country in one trip than most Panamanians would over the entire course of their lifetime.

I didn't worry about my financial circumstances. Life is risk. After purchasing my plane tickets, I had exactly $1000 in cash for my ten-day trip and that was it. Credit cards were not widely accepted in Panama yet. If I ran out of cash, I was fucked. When I returned from Panama I would be flat broke. Trusting that everything would work out, I said "fuck it," and hopped on the plane.

Everyone who heard I was traveling alone to Central America was petrified. I was thoroughly pumped to get out of the punishing Midwest cold and into a long overdue adventure beneath the warm sun. I couldn't wait to rack up another stamp in my passport.

When the plane touched down at PTY, I sprinted

from the gate to immigration out of habit. First in line, I breezed right through. Rolling my clothes tight as spools of thread to fit in my carry-ons, I had no luggage to retrieve. The humid stickiness was a welcome departure from St. Louis' freezing temperatures.

My taxi arrived and we sped down the Corredor Sur to Albrook airport to catch my flight to Bocas. The Panama skyline was a sight to see, with the city asleep and the streetlights scant. It gave me a feeling of mischievousness, a secret shared with the universe.

Landing in Bocas del Toro felt surreal. Only a few short months ago I had been there under abhorrent circumstances, with a completely different mindset. It was liberating to return as a free woman.

Backpack strapped on and pulling my blue roller behind me, I pushed through the tinted glass doors to the outside of the airport. The sunshine hit my sparkling spirit and bounced off like a prism. It was as if Bocas had marinated in rose-colored champagne all night. I felt fantastic.

I spent the morning meeting with business owners in Bocas Town discussing tourism opportunities. The rest of the time in Bocas was full-on holiday mode. Waking up in a tropical paradise, I would stroll along the hot black pavement of Bocas Town to Fat Boy Treats for fresh homemade donuts and robust coffee, making friends along the way.

Quirky Island Bob wore typical tropical T-shirts and lived in a hut on an overgrown neighboring island while he crafted a party boat from scraps he'd collected. From time to time, backpackers looking for room and board would join him.

Carter was an engineer working in Trinidad, and partying in Bocas del Toro. He called himself a Zonian, meaning he was born within the Panama Canal zone. Carter was the epitome of island shenanigans, always finding a group of vacationing chicks - often in their birthday suits - to party on his boat, the Evil Jaeger.

Clad in a leopard print bikini and over-sized sunglasses, I clutched a vodka tonic and sunbathed on the Evil Jaeger, as we bounced over the waves of the Caribbean Sea. Lynyrd Skynyrd was our soundtrack as we lounged in the crystal clear waters of Starfish Beach.

Carter's friends on a luxury Catamaran cruise invited us to dinner and we happily accepted, joining them for lobster pasta, and lots of champagne underneath the stars. I felt like I was really living. I was happy.

My last day in Bocas, I stopped by Lemongrass restaurant before catching my flight. Lo and behold, I found Cheyenne inside! It was the perfect ending to a marvelous weekend. Once Cheyenne recognized me, she smiled broadly.

"What are you doing here? How are you? You look great, you're so happy!" she said, astounded to see me. We settled around a large round table near the back of the open-air restaurant, overlooking the water and reminisced about the wedding, commiserating over its absurdities, and hugging when Cheyene expressed her heartfelt happiness for me. It was clear I had evolved to a completely different place than the life I was trapped in when we first met. She too had a career change, leaving her former place of employment for a different opportunity, while building a brand-new restaurant on Bastimentos Island. It was a time of change for everyone, I realized. And change was always good.

Back on the mainland, it was clear that Panama City was on the verge of something exciting. Evolving from a third-world country into a world-class metropolis at light speed, it showed signs of multiple personalities. The Panama Metro, the first subway in Central America, would offer futuristic, air-conditioned transportation as an alternative to the crumbling pedestrian sidewalks. Impressive skyscrapers undergoing construction in the city center received mail with addresses including 'near the old KFC' or 'across from the coconut tree.' Not much was logical or precise about Panama. Not yet, at least.

Checking into the Panamericana Hostel, the air was thick, as the hostel had no air conditioning. Two ceiling fans that had seen better days rotated noisily above me. Occasionally, a slight breeze would flow through the translucent curtains adorning two sets of open French doors that led to a wraparound balcony. A strange man in only his boxers slept on top of the sheets about five feet from me, breathing heavily through his mouth.

My bed was equipped with a sparsely fluffed pillow and one thin sheet to cover up with. It didn't matter, as I would sleep for only a few hours per night. Most of my nights would be spent writing on the veranda beneath the stars.

It was early morning and I had the rest of the day to explore so I headed out on foot with my backpack. Walking along the Amador Causeway in the morning sun, everything was still new to me, as my last trip to Panama City left me distracted at all times. Now I was free to take it all in, undisturbed.

Visiting the local fish market at Mercado de Meriscos was not for the faint of heart. Everything was overwhelming: the smells, the noise, the crowd. I purchased a scoop of tangy, fresh ceviche from a gritty vendor for a few USD and sat on the dock watching fishing boats slowly ebb into the harbor. Devouring the Styrofoam cup of ceviche with a plastic fork, it was ten times better than any served in fancy fine dining establishments in the States.

My trek took me across the street toward residential neighborhoods for a different perspective. Halfway across the bridge, the sun called me back toward the Panama Bay to take a photo of the sparkling waterfront. Pushing my sunglasses to the top of my head, I squinted into the glared screen of my camera as it went from blurred to focused.

I realized I was staring at Fountain Plaza on the Amador Causeway. It was where Dmitri and I had once stood, smiling, kissing, and living.

A twinge of melancholy ached in my heart.

Lifting my face toward the sun, I tightened the straps of my backpack and crossed the bridge and hit a left.

The Avenida Central street market moved at a rapid pace. Located in a less-than-glamorous neighborhood, shabbily-maintained stores peddled cheap clothing and bric-a-brac, shopkeepers loudly negotiating with customers. Lean-to fruit and vegetable stands sold rainbows on each corner and the aroma of ethnic cuisine pooled saliva in my cheeks.

Sweating ladies fanned themselves while sitting behind folding tables covered in Panamanian lottery tickets. A flamboyant troupe of kids put on a raucous performance, causing a crowd to gather. I had no idea what was going on. It was all in rapid Spanish.

It was clear to the local Panamanians that I was an outsider. My pale skin tone gave it away immediately. Most glanced my way but did not speak or acknowledge me, almost as if I didn't exist. I often enjoyed this slight isolation while traveling. I was a true fly on the wall. Simply passing through, giving up my life and living theirs for a while. Submersed in a typical day in the real barrios of Panama, I happily people watched from beneath my invisibility cloak.

The air was especially muggy that evening, as I smoked a cigarette in the common area of the hostel. A faint breeze trickling in from the four large open windows provided little relief. I parted with a few Balboas that were given to me as change at the market and popped open an ice-cold Coca-Cola, leaning my head back and pressing the frosty glass bottle to my neck and chest for relief from the sweltering temperatures before taking a sip.

A local told me about a breakdancing battle taking place at a club in Casco Viejo called Teatro Amador. I had to be there. Walking in the general right direction, I only solicited two people for help before stumbling across the venue. Stepping in the long line, I turned to a teen next to me.

"How much is the show?" I asked.

"Cover is two Balboas," he responded automatically. Doing a double take, he looked me up and down, evaluating my dainty dress and sandals, unsure if I belonged. "Do you know this is a hip-hop show?"

I smiled and nodded, amused. "Yes, I'm aware."

Shuffling my way up the line, I entered a bar packed with all varieties of people. B-Boys and B-Girls, young kids, dreadheads, mainstream professionals, backpackers, island hoppers—they were all there together, having a blast. A DJ blared classic hip-hop while waiting for the breakdancing battle to begin, even mixing in the Beastie Boys.

The show was sick. After the breakdancing battle winner was crowned, I stepped outside and the lights of Teatro Amador faded behind me as I headed down the deserted street. I was alone and free once again.

It was quietly thrilling. I can often be found out wandering the streets alone during the offbeat hours while traveling in a foreign land. Seeking that soft silence, feeling the stories it has to tell. Being alive.

Purposefully choosing a questionable path back to the hostel, I was greeted with vibrant graffiti at every turn. On a mission to inspire myself with street art, I dashed around in the dark, snapping photos of Super Mario mushrooms and scrawled sage advice. Paying absolutely no attention to where I was going, I followed a ten-foot tall armadillo masterpiece the length of a stone wall down a dark alley, dead-ending into a drop off of murky water.

A neon sign hung in the window of a tiny store, illuminating a hodge-podge of dusty stones, tourist trinkets, and wide-brimmed Panama Hats.

I felt like I should go in. It was too perfect not to. Stepping inside, a melodic voice sang out to me in the most beautiful Spanish, "Buenas, gringa. Yo sabía que ibas a venir."

I didn't know where it was coming from or what the words meant but it made me smile. Dipping my hands into a pile of turquoise gems and rubbing my thumb over their smooth curves, I responded using most of my Spanish vocabulary in one sentence. "Lo siento. No español. Sólo Inglés. Por favor."

An older woman appeared behind the counter next to an antiquated cash register. Long wispy gray hair was twisted into a loose fishbone braid hanging past her shoulders. Deep-set wrinkles formed around her dark eyes and bright pink-painted mouth. There was something peculiar about the way she looked at me. I couldn't quite put my finger on it.

Settling on three gemstones, I brought them to the counter.

"Where are you from?" she asked, ignoring my purchases.

"Estados Unidos," I said.

"And your age?"

"Perdon?" I asked, confused.

"Your age?" she asked again, her eyebrows raised

in anticipation.

I had no idea why she wanted to know my age.

"Well, I'll be twenty-nine next month. December seventeenth. I'm a Sagittarius."

"Just as I thought. Happy early birthday," she said, her lips turning into a knowing smile.

Just as I thought." What does that mean?

"Gracias," I said, perplexed.

"You will soon receive your best gift. Saturn Return. I felt it when you walked in. It happens at twenty-nine." she said, nodding.

"Saturn Return. Huh. Okay," I said, smiling and turning my eyes sideways in skepticism. I liked to read my horoscope but I didn't know much about astrology. "I'll look it up. How much do I owe you?"

"Nada. Feliz cumpleaños! La verdad es la hija del tiempo. Suerte." She waved me off with what I assumed were birthday wishes and our conversation faded to the back of my mind.

The next few days were balls-to-the-wall busy. A morning coffee meeting on the roof deck started my day with the most beautiful view of the sparkling Bay of Panama. It took me three taxi rides and knocking on two wrong doors to make my way to a portfolio viewing with Panama's top photographer. Jetting back downtown, I cooled off with a fresh fruit smoothie while learning about precious cameo jewelry carved from Central American conch shells.

My last day in the country, I took a trip to Portobelo, a remote town with a colorful history, most famously known as the historical site where Pirate Captain Morgan—yes, *the* Captain Morgan—captured the city in 1668. The purpose was to visit El Otro Lado, a posh private retreat.

Accessible only by water taxi, beauty abounded every inch of the grounds. Luscious strands of thick green grass met the calmly lapping ocean waters. Climbing a slight hill led me to a secluded waterfall. El Otro Lado was by far my absolute favorite place in the entire country of Panama. I vowed to return for longer than an afternoon.

An all-inclusive resort near Panama City was my last hurrah, where I played fancy traveler in a white and gold bandeau bikini, lounging on the beach, digging my toes beneath the white sand to keep cool. Diving into the crashing waves every so often, the sun dried droplets of water from my now-tanned body as I sipped on a frozen strawberry daiquiri, my mouth fixed in a permanent smile. Sleeping on the over-sized, plush king mattress was quite a difference from the thin springy hostel cot, but I loved them both the same.

Traveling home from Panama the next morning, I gazed out of the window of the plane as the country disappeared into the clouds. I was doing the right thing with my life. I loved traveling and adventuring. Meeting new people and writing about my experiences made me happy.

Stepping off of the plane and into the stinging cold reality in St. Louis was rough. I was out of money. Panama hadn't quenched my desires for travel and adventure. It had only intensified them. As soon as I landed at Lambert Airport, I was ready to leave again.

I booked a flight to Europe for a month or so later with a nested weekend trip in the United Kingdom to attend a travel conference, hoping to drum up some business for Panama. Bumming around the Netherlands before and after, I had an adventure to look forward to. I was positive the money situation would figure itself out.

And it did.

In need of cash but unwilling to commit my days

chained to an office, I began to offer my services as a consultant instead of accepting permanent, full-time positions. Bingo.

Snowed-in, baking chocolate chip cookies at home, I turned twenty-nine. My conversation with the Panamanian lady in her little shop of wonders popped into my head. I Googled Saturn Return.

Saturn Return occurs when the planet Saturn reaches the exact degree in the universe that it was when you were born, roughly at twenty-nine-and-a-half years of age. It is a crossroads when life-altering decisions are made, putting you face-to-face with your fears and reminding you that it's never too late to be who you were meant to be.

Unearthing a purpose for the upheaval in my life, I realized I had unknowingly embraced Saturn Return over the past few months. Not resisting the changes but working through them, I was evolving. One block at a time, a yellow brick road appeared in front of me. I didn't know exactly where it was going but I didn't need to.

My passion for writing had been renewed, the characters, storyline, and purpose now crystal-clear in my head. I was born to be a writer, my medium to create, to share my story, my view, my experiences. I had all the time in the world but was light years behind my mind. Every free minute from then on was spent writing.

One February morning I traded my cold climate for another more than 4,000 miles away, jumping on a nine-hour flight to Amsterdam with no set agenda other than to wander around the country exploring, get stoned, visit the Anne Frank House, party with Felix, and spend time enjoying life while writing outside storybook cafes. I was so caught up in my consulting projects that I hadn't taken the time to plan anything beforehand. I had no hotel reservations, no airport pickup, and didn't even have a map. I also had no worries. I would figure it out.

Landing at Amsterdam Airport Schiphol around 6:30 am, I traced my finger over the public transportation map displayed beneath dirty glass at the main terminal and bought a ticket to Amsterdam's Centraal Station. Centraal Station was almost as daunting as the massive Zhuhai Underground. I walked in circles around the hurried tunneled corridors for at least fifteen minutes before finally discovering the way out.

Standing outside the train station in the struggling European winter sunrise, I admired the skyline of seventeenth century buildings across the way. I made eye contact with Gamal, a man exiting the train station. Squat and dark as night expat from South Africa, Gamal had been living in Amsterdam for three years. He led me to a reputable shop down the intimate streets of Kalverstraat market to buy a SIM card and *voila*! I had a working phone.

Not much was open yet since it was so early, but the coffee shops were and that was perfecto.

"Do you smoke?" Gamal asked.

"I'm in Amsterdam. What do you think?" I asked rhetorically.

Gamal showed me to the counter of a coffeeshop where I chose from a list of marijuana strains, uppers and downers, mid-grades to high-grades, but no reggie. The staff weighed out a few grams of White Widow and dropped them into a clear Ziploc bag with green pot leaves printed on the sides. Thin white rolling papers were dispensed freely from a small stand to the left of the scale.

Taking a seat at a square table next to a shiny purple hookah, we shared a wake-and-bake joint although I hadn't slept yet, tiny servings of cafe lattes most Americans would consider insufficient, and wafers of shortbread over a bit of light conversation. He was a Rastafarian who left me with recommendations for hotels, directions to the Anne Frank House, and a map of the best Dutch food on the way.

After squeezing behind the secret bookcase and climbing the narrow stairs to Anne Frank's attic, I people-watched at tea tables outside in the brisk February air while devouring Dutch waffles drenched in sickly-sweet chocolate and powdered sugar. The Netherlands was a whole new world to me and I spent the next few days as a sponge, soaking up everything I could. People on bicycles whizzed past me dinging bells dressed in suits and skirts, their tires pounding over the cobblestone.

Strolling through museums and traveling art exhibits held in ancient cathedrals, I experienced the Dutch culture on foot through streets and gangways, canals and quaint squares. Perusing shopping plazas big and small, wares high-end and black market, I knocked out a good chunk of historical landmarks, making sure to diversify my tourist traps with oddities such as the Condomerie, a store boasting a huge collection of art about contraception. I purchased a few custom condoms as gifts, which mature-looking women wrapped individually in brightly-colored paper.

Rounding out my eccentric curiosities, I stumbled upon the Museum of Prostitution, nestled between two brothels overlooking the canal. It was supposedly the only of its kind in the world. A viewing room draped in red velvet from floor-to-ceiling looped a short film on the lives of the more than 1,000 working girls (and guys) in the Red Light District. Many clocked eleven hours a day, six days a week. An average client visit was about seven minutes.

Photographs and personal accounts filled in the

blanks for those who were curious about the attraction to prostitution; they unsurprisingly revealed an assortment of liberation and desperation. Entering the museum's replica of a €150 per shift room rental, I was immediately illuminated in the red hue surrounding the clear glass. Revealing a terrific view of De Wallen, I was also met with glowing pairs of eyes staring back at me, window shopping.

It was unnerving.

Back on the cobblestone streets I ran into Amsterdam's own Marijuana, Hemp and Hash Museum just down the road, which, strangely enough, displayed a hemp bag made in good old St. Louis, Missouri, USA alongside a humongous crystal-covered marijuana plant.

My lodging for the trip would come in a variety of typical drifter accommodations. Unlocking nondescript alleyway doors with skeleton keys and climbing creaky steps of spiral staircases as steep as they were narrow to the top floors of boutique hotels built in 1725 was my idea of an ideal European trip. The living quarters were often charmingly bare-boned with olde-world windows opening to the outside and devoid of screens.

The first night, a hotel staffer gave me a Hobbit-like suite at hostel prices. Located at what seemed like a tower atop the historic building, it was accessible by miniature ladder and complete with a Jacuzzi hot tub overlooking the city. Jet lagged, I tapped away on my laptop at odd hours while lounging in a bubble bath listening to Marvin Gaye and smoking a joint, watching the blossom of the sunrise unfold over the sky. Each time I think I can't get a better vista, I fly to a new place.

The country smeared past me backwards as the train moved from Amsterdam back to Schiphol

Airport, where I flew to the United Kingdom for the weekend. Arriving at London Heathrow Airport with backpack in hand, first up was the tourism conference in Birmingham. Riding the train north to the Birmingham's National Exhibition Center, I made the rounds and exhausted the vendors and attendees in just an hour, scuttling back to London with zero prospects. Although travel industry insiders in Panama assured me Europeans were dying to visit Central America, the show was a bust. Oh well. Gary and I would course correct when I returned to the States.

Minding the gap, I had just enough time to make a Beatles Walking Tour of London, catching the Underground subway system to Tottenham Court Road Station then hiking over to Dominion Theatre, dodging cherry red double-decker buses along the way. The tour guide named Richard, who resembled an Oompa-Loompa in size, stature, and entertainment value, was collecting payment when I arrived. Nine jingling pounds from each guest, he zipped the heavy coins into his sagging fanny pack.

We relived Beatle mania, searching for Paul McCartney around his office grounds, marveling over the studio where *Hey Jude* was recorded, and taking photos crossing Abbey Road. After the tour ended, I headed to my hostel for check-in, strolling down Jermyn Street, a classic London avenue filled with Mercedes-Benz driven by chauffeurs, escorting their aristocratic clients to gourmet cafes, patisseries and luxury gown and haberdashery outfitters.

The Abracadabra hostel was hidden in plain sight. Passing through intimidating dark wooden doors and following multicolored stairs down into a dimly-lit basement, the Russian staff was friendly yet showed little emotion. I was given bed number eight out of twelve. A chilling draft seeped in from beneath the window and the lumpy mattress sagged in the middle.

I had slept on worse. Pulling my laptop from my bag, I began to write.

My alarm went off at 7:00 am. After hitting the prerequisites of Buckingham Palace, Big Ben, Wimbledon, Regent Park Zoo, St. Paul's Cathedral, and Hampton Court efficiently via a thirty-minute loop around the London Eye, Camden Market was my next conquest.

It wasn't a long trip and I enjoyed the rural scenery. Upon arrival, I exited the train in the throes of the masses and hiked up the steps to street level. The vibes felt eclectic and welcoming, the definition of a melting pot.

Wanna-be Banksys illustrated the cobblestone streets where trendy fashion havens were neighbors with tourist shops and boasted basement S&M dungeons. Whatever was sought could be found in Camden Market, whether the golden treasure be knee-high designer fishnets, soft and warm homemade double Rocky Road English fudge, a secondhand Jack Kerouac novel on fifty percent discount, savory Shanghai steamed dumplings, or a long-hair fur Natasha-style Russian hat—all of which I purchased within an hour or so. It was the perfect outing.

I spent a few hours meandering through the gypsy market, mulling over my stimulated senses. Strong sunrays kept the biting cold at bay until dusk. Tupac's poetry blasted down the aisles of wooden vendor booths. It reminded me of home.

After picking up a few small pieces of art, the sun was gone and a chill crept in around my collar. I hopped on the Underground headed to Covent Garden, where juggling street performers and classic string quartets put on a show for a pence or two in front of the outdoor cafe tables.

Everyone was staring at me, as I was wearing my newly purchased, extra-warm and hard-to-miss

Russian fur hat. I didn't care.

Wandering around stone-bricked side streets, my path led me to the Mysteries of Covent Garden astrology shop, shrouded in an inviting energy. Making my way inside, a mini Buddha meditation garden left me speechless. The calmness it exuded rushed into me.

Around the corner from the garden sat a glass chest of precious stones. Above it, the word Tarot caught my third eye. A beautiful, petite Asian lady with jet-black hair and narrow-rimmed glasses stood nearby.

"Can you provide me with a little more detail regarding the tarot readings? I've done a few in the past. Some were okay. Some weren't. I don't like when they ask me what I want to know." I said firmly.

The tarot reading was calling me and I was willing, but not if it was going to be a waste of time. I didn't know what I wanted to know. I just wanted to be told. Something. About me. Something I didn't know. Something I wasn't aware I should be focusing on. Something beneath the surface or over my head. Something new, to enlighten me. I wanted to evolve. I needed more.

"Ahh, Neil would be excellent for you. He's been doing tarot and working with spirituality for over a quarter of a century. You don't have to say a word if you don't want to. If you don't feel like you're connecting after the first ten minutes, you can leave and I'll give you a refund," she assured me.

I handed over a wad of Euros and climbed the cramped stairwell to the third floor where a thin man with a scant spattering of hair emerged from a corner room.

"Welcome, please come in," he smiled warmly.

I did, taking a seat in one of the two chairs tucked beneath a wooden table.

The first card pulled was the publisher.

"Most importantly," he said, "you must know you are supposed to write, if you aren't already. You are a writer."

Second was the strength card.

"You're extremely self-sufficient and this has been detrimental to relationships in the past. Know that these were your partner's fallacies, not yours. You were always meant to transcend them." This was an especially poignant and welcome observation. He looked into my eyes and said, "You are where you are supposed to be."

Peering over the table and astounded by what he saw once the last card was set in place, Neil was giddy with excitement.

"My, my, you have performed an immense amount of introspective work over the past few years, Miss Emily!" he said, incredulously. Scrunching his eyebrows at the cards, his tone softened. "You've also followed through with some tough changes in your life recently." He looked to me for confirmation.

I nodded slightly in agreement.

He continued, his voice rising with each sentence, "The way your cards align, you have the best reading I've seen in years. There is an extreme amount of positive energy and activity surrounding you. The manifestation is well on its way. Everything is on the right path. It will all be revealed quite nicely . . . soon, very soon, you can be sure of that. Simply allow the river to keep flowing. I have no other advice for you. You're very spiritually advanced, you know—"

I couldn't tell if he was asking a question or making a statement.

"Most people don't make it to this stage. Ever. And you are so young," he marveled. "How old are you?"

"I just turned twenty-nine," I responded.

His face lit up in recognition. "Ahh, Saturn Return, my dear. I should have known."

Saturn Return again! I leaned forward, eager to learn more about this mysterious life-transforming planet.

"You welcomed Saturn Return, discarded the old, forged into the new, and are powering through your evolution like no other. You are on track to becoming the ultimate you, who is happy, fulfilled, and successful," he said plainly.

Once I began to speak, we got along famously. Neil assured me my life was headed in a fantastic direction.

"Often," he said, his face somber, "people make it to Saturn Return but have already locked themselves into commitments such as schooling for a certain career, a young marriage, or the responsibility of children. And once they realize their true self, purpose, and path to happiness, they're too afraid to change their circumstances to pursue it. But not you," he paused and looked at me over his spectacles, the light reflecting off of his nearly bald head. "You are one in a billion."

I left walking as if my feet were kissing the earth. Everything was coming together, I could feel it. It had been. The tarot was just confirmation - a bit of extra encouragement to keep moving forward. Everything would be fantastic.

That evening I strolled about the cobblestone streets underneath the bright London lights, taking it all in. It was a decidedly romantic and magical city, leaving me longing for the right hand to hold and soul to squeeze. I would return, but not likely alone. Jack Kerouac kept me company at Heathrow until it was time to cross the pond back to the Netherlands.

Felix and I planned to meet in Amsterdam and continue on to The Hague to visit our friend

Benjamin. We had tickets for a big surf party on Old Scheveningen Beach that weekend. I was stoked.

Carefully crossing the Amsterdam Centraal train tracks with my backpack, I walked toward the Red Light District. Ringing Felix, he apologized that he was still at work, promising to call me back soon. An uneasy feeling washed over me, since it was already late evening and he was a three-and-a-half-hour train ride away. I was used to being alone, but being alone unexpectedly late at night was a different story.

I assessed the situation. Two guys stood to my left outside of Baba, a popular coffee shop. One was on the phone attempting to navigate for a friend. The other was helping, but not much.

I made eye contact. "Trying to give directions?"

"Yes, it's not working," he said. I took a few steps closer.

"It's really busy in there," I said, as I motioned inside the smoky establishment.

"Yes, Friday night." He had an English accent. "What's your name?"

"Emily. And yours?"

"Craig. Nice to meet you."

His friend then introduced himself, sticking his hand out to shake. "Hi, I'm Craig."

I grasped his hand, but then said, "Wait, so you're both named Craig?"

Craig #1 smiled. "Yes, and wait 'till you see this!" He looked over at two guys who just exited Baba, waving them over. "This is Craig, and Craig," he said, introducing me to two more men. I laughed. We all laughed. I was glad for the relaxation, if only momentary.

They were from the UK, in Amsterdam for Craig #2's weekend stag party. Craig #3 handed me a pre-rolled joint in a plastic case as they moved on to the next bar.

"What is it? Is it hash or weed or what?" I had never smoked hashish before. I definitely did not want to start when I was alone wandering the streets of Amsterdam, not knowing where I would be sleeping that night.

He shrugged his shoulders as if to say 'I don't know.' I thought about it for a millisecond and took it anyway. When somebody offers me a free, fat ass joint from a coffee shop in Amsterdam, I take that shit and smoke it. And I did, lighting it up right then.

Happy to have received the gift of unknown substance, I moseyed on down the street puffing away, meaning to put it out after a minute or two. Caught up people watching, it burned right down to the filter.

I wandered in circles. The mystery joint began taking effect in an unfamiliar way, tickling the crooks of my brain. A wave of sedation washed over me like a strong current and slight paranoia dripped into my thought stream. I hoped the joint was just hashish and that it wouldn't fuck me up too badly.

People were staring at me strangely everywhere I went. Men fixed their eyes on me, maybe more than usual, or maybe I was just trippin'. Either way, I didn't like it. I was entirely too high to be wandering the streets of a foreign country alone.

My mouth was extra parched. Aimlessly searching the streets, a man locked gazes with me and continued to stare when I looked away. As I passed he reached out, grabbing my arm and pulling me toward the bar yelling "Come party with us, sexy!"

Snatching my arm back as his buddies pulled him inside, I felt like prey, with everyone ready and waiting. To do something. To me. I didn't know what. My heart raced as I attempted to wet my Sahara desert of a mouth. I prayed not to have an anxiety attack.

I took refuge in the Medieval Torture Museum. The lobby was deserted and looked like a quiet space for me to chill out for a minute and regain my composure. Also, they had small glass bottles of Coca-Cola for sale. I was so thirsty, and could use a spike in blood sugar.

I grabbed a Coke and approached the counter, handing over twenty euros for a museum ticket and the drink. The attendant was Russian. He seemed to be undergoing an internal struggle about complying with my request.

"What time do you close? If it's too late, I don't need to go in. I'll just take the Coke," I said, desperately.

He shook his head. "No, no. Customer first." He consulted at the clock. It read 9:45 pm. I assumed they closed fifteen minutes later.

"Oh no, really, it's okay if you close at ten. I'll just take the Coke."

"No, no. It's my pleasure. Customer first. Please enjoy the museum." He handed me a ticket and a few euros in change, guiding me toward the first floor of exhibits.

Reluctantly, I made my way up the stairwell and was immediately surrounded by large torture devices on all sides. They were lying out in the middle of the floor with no protective covering, not behind glass, and in absence of 'Do Not Touch' signs. Nothing separated me from the rusty Spike Collars, ancient dull-bladed Guillotines, and iron Head Vices contorted to fit shrunken skulls.

Posters on the wall explained each instrument of torture, what crime it served as punishment for, who administered it, during what time period, and any famous people it was used upon. I learned about Long Stork Stems, inserted into the anus of a person lying on their stomach, then set upright allowing gravity to take over, with the tortured sliding down on a skewer until all of their internal organs were ruptured and destroyed, resulting in death.

It started to get a bit creepy as I continued on. Still semi-trippin' from the mystery joint, I concluded the Torture Museum was probably not the best environment to calm down from a freak out. I was a little sketched out but reminded myself it was just a museum. Even though I was the only person there, it was just a building with old artifacts, the likes of which I would probably never have the opportunity to see in person again.

A wooden Iron Maiden box sat invitingly in the corner. Tall enough to enclose an average-sized human, pointed spears protruded from the interior, piercing the imprisoned. They would be left to bleed out for days, as the spikes were strategically placed to avoid puncturing any vital body parts, resulting in prolonged death and maximum torture. Its door swung open just enough to poke my head in and look around, so I did.

Lost in an imagined world of medieval torture, I wondered what it would be like to be sentenced to the Iron Maiden box, entering with apprehension and forced to wait with gloom slowly closing in on me.

In real life, the lights began to dim. I heard them click off one by one, eventually blanketing the entire museum in darkness. My eyes opened wide as saucers and every hair on my body stood on end. I immediately jumped away from the relic, terrified someone would push me in the Iron Maiden and torture me to death. Stumbling backwards over what I remembered to be a stained executioner's sickle, I yelped as I fell to the floor, losing my grip on the glass Coke bottle that promptly shattered.

Covered in tacky syrup and unable to see in the dark, I freaked out. Scrambling to stand, I carefully slid my feet forward in the direction of the front door, crunching over the shards of glass.

"Hello?"

No one responded but I heard the unmistakable click of a deadbolt sliding into place. I swallowed a huge lump in my throat, scared as shit.

Nudging one foot in front of the other, I shuffled through the darkness to the stairs, using a long, rotting wooden torture table as my guide. Once my hands gripped the stairwell banister, I jumped down to the first floor and raced to the door, pounding on it as soon as my fists could reach.

"Hello! Hey! What the fuck!" I yelled desperately at the top of my lungs. "Hey!" Looking out the window, I saw the Russian museum attendant climbing on his bike to head home for the evening. I banged on the door again, louder. Thankfully, he heard me and turned his head back. Recognizing that there was still someone in the building, he rushed to open the door.

"I'm so sorry!" he exclaimed. "I forgot! Please enjoy the museum."

"What the *fuck*, dude! You just fucking locked me in the motherfucking torture museum! That was fucking scary as shit!" I attempted to move past him, more than ready to get the hell out of there. He stepped in front of me.

"I forgot you were here. I will turn on the lights and wait. I'm sorry."

"No, no, fuck that. I'm out!" I ducked under his arm, running out the door. He called after me but I didn't turn back.

I received a message from Felix informing me he wouldn't make it to Amsterdam that evening but would meet me the next morning for our trip to The Hague. Drained from the night's misadventure, I booked a tiny room at the next hotel I came across. It was filled with loud stag parties but I didn't care. There was a lock on the door, fluffy blanket and pillow on the bed.

After refreshing myself in the shower no bigger than a phone booth, I ran out for a Dutch waffle and downer OG Cali Kush to help me relax. Returning to my cozy abode, I pulled open the windows. Sounds and smells of Amsterdam filled the room, the hustle and bustle and kush in the air. Powering on my laptop, I lit a joint and began to write, glancing down at the lively streets every so often. The words poured from my fingertips into the early hours of the morning, outlasting most of the Red Light District patrons.

I woke up in my shitty hotel room at 9:00 am exhausted and feeling slightly off from the mystery joint and Cali Kush. Intending on closing my eyes for just a moment, the maid knocked on the door, startling me to consciousness. I checked the time. *Shit.* It was 10:50 am. I had to meet Felix at 11:00 am.

Throwing on jeans and a sweater, I grabbed my bags and made my way to Amsterdam Centraal Station. Suffering through a three-and-a-half hour train ride, Felix finally arrived. I hadn't seen him since Cologne, over a year ago.

"Ems!" he shouted, waving to me with a big grin on his face.

"Hi Felix!" We threw our arms around each other. Time had done him well. Wearing skinny jeans, tennis shoes, polo sweater and brown leather jacket, he carried a backpack identical to mine. His dirty blonde hair was shaggy, typical for Felix, and greenish brown eyes warm and friendly.

Wading through the busy station, we grabbed a few beers for the ride before hopping on another train together, catching up along the way.

"Whatever happened with you and Click!?" he asked.

I hadn't properly explained the situation to him so I gave him a brief overview, highlighting some of the more shocking incidents, and expressing nostalgia for the way things were. It turned out that Felix and Rune's relationship had been a bit rocky since the fire extinguisher incident in Cologne.

"What about you? What have you been up to?" I asked.

His photography career was taking off, he was a bona fide doctor, working as a general practitioner. Creating and maintaining, his days were never boring and he was always in control. Felix's life did not pass him by or happen to him. On the contrary, Felix happened to things; Felix happened to life.

The Hague was only an hour train ride from Amsterdam. Benjamin greeted us wearing black leggings and a blue running jacket, his bright blonde curly hair pulled into a messy bun. A small 'b' tattoo adorned Benjamin's hand to remind him to 'be present.' I loved his outlook on life.

His house was literally an office building. In the Netherlands, if a commercial building is empty for a certain period of time, a group of people are offered the opportunity to live in and maintain the buildings, paying low rent. The beachfront property had been open for over two years, so Benjamin and his friends had a stable place to call home for quite some time.

Entering the lobby through large glass doors, we made our way up to the front desk. The floors were tile, just as any other office building would be. The hallway opened into the large cafeteria where Benjamin's roommates were found, lounging around drinking wine and puffing on cigarettes as smoky veils hung in the air.

Tygo limped into the kitchen, his right leg and knee smashed to smithereens from a scooter accident during he and Benjamin's big Southeast Asia backpacking trip the summer before. I could relate, and we bonded over shared stories of scooter terror.

Accidentally smoking heroin in Vietnam, Tygo and Benjamin wandered the dirt roads late at night fucked out of their minds but living to tell the hilarious tale.

Esmee and her boyfriend Julian were the bee's knees. Julian, a psychiatrist who worked with mentally disabled homeless, was also a surfer and drummer in a rock band. Esmee was a doctor with a gorgeous mind and kick-ass surfer with an infectious smile. Ultra confident, she wore a black sweater over a white button up shirt with the collar tucked in, skinny black pants and black tennis shoes with a white swoosh. Her beautiful caramel toffee hair was pinned up at the nape of her neck, muddy brown eyes painted in black and Audrey Hepburn pout adorned with bright red lipstick that looked absolutely divine.

As the night wore on, we became fast friends. Esmee was so down-to-earth and genuine. If I ever had a girl crush, it was her.

Navigating around the marina on foot, we mobbed out to the surf party after midnight. It was bitterly cold and windy and the rain wasn't helping. My light jacket that worked so well in Amsterdam didn't cut it in The Hague.

Despite the bone-chilling temperatures, the seaside party was legit. I had an inkling of what it would be like when Felix asked if I wanted to go, since he and Benjamin were serious partiers. It was hardcore.

A reggae-ska band rocked out onstage beneath a white tent flailing about in the wind, fighting a losing battle against Mother Nature. Ten feet from the stage a sea of people danced and sang, their bodies waving back and forth in unison.

A bright red bouncy house stuffed past maximum capacity bobbed along with the beat, slowly deflating under the weight of the crowd. We stood in the middle of everything. The ground was covered in a layer of plastic cups, bottles, and trash. Hippies, soccer moms, surfers, grandparents, dreadheads, and people who didn't give a shit what they looked like proliferated. I absolutely loved it.

Esmee and I were cold so we walked up the uneven, wooden steps to the inside of the DJ tent while the guys braved the wind for the end of the band's set.

"I hope they play nineties music!" Esmee said excitedly in her cute Dutch accent.

I laughed. "Sure, sounds good."

Europeans.

As the DJ started, she and I were having a blast moving our bodies to the beat without a care in the world. Eventually Benjamin joined us, his long blonde ringlets flying around. His hair kept getting stuck in my lip gloss and we screamed in laughter.

After the live band ended, the dance floor flooded. Everybody was just trying to have a good time. People pushed me, spilled beer on my clothes, stepped on my boots, elbowed me in the back, and ashed cigarettes in my hair. I almost got upset, but realized nobody else was—not one single person.

We jammed for hours, reminiscing and dancing to decades-old songs, drinking from tiny cups, and cheesing until our faces ached. Music pounded through the tall speakers, the bass reverberating in my chest, one of my all-time favorite feelings. Green laser lights bounced around the tent as if we were on set of the old J. Lo video from "Waiting for Tonight."

Fog billowed from a smoke machine, transporting us to a mystical discotheque. Multicolored lights twirled from the ceiling, twinkling and glinting a prism of colors over our bodies as we danced the night away. A little after 4:00 am the last song played: "Africa" by ToTo. We sang our hearts out as a group, with Felix holding the air mic for me, belting the last line together until we had no air left to breathe.

It was some of the most fun I've had in twenty-nine years.

The walk home was unforgivably frigid. Party-goers of all ages zoomed past us on their bicycles. The diversity of people and mode of transportation tickled me. Differences such as that are exactly why I travel.

Snuggling up in a fluffy white comforter atop an air mattress Benjamin prepared for me, I threw the blanket over my head, cocooning myself in the down. It was 6:00 am and the sun was coming up, shining brightly through the wall of windows next to me.

Awakening four hours later, it was difficult to keep my eyes open and my head was wobbly on my neck. I wanted to sleep for a year and a day.

Benjamin greeted me.

"Good morning, sunshine! Would you like some oatmeal? I'm about to make breakfast." His mood was upbeat and cheerful in only the way a Dutchie can be after a night of drinking.

I definitely wanted oatmeal. "Um, hell yes. Thank you."

I felt so very shitty and was having a hard time thinking so I decided to press the restart button by taking a shower first. Washing off the beer, smoke, dirt, sweat, sand, and general Hague-funk from the party was essential. I was pretty gross.

A five-minute wash later, I was clad in skinny pants and a teal sweater with my hair in a mop of wet curls. I made my way down the end of the hallway to Benjamin's Picasso-shaped breakfast nook. A dark wood credenza covered an entire wall, festooned with a curious display of objet d'art, among them antique cameras, sundries from traveling, an espresso machine, and a stack of thick hardcover gold-gilded books filled with glossy photos of surfers, climbers, and thousands of words detailing history.

A brown leather couch faced a view of creamy

vanilla sand edged neatly against the robin's-egg blue marine. Separating the lounge area from the breakfast nook was a vintage desk with a turntable perched atop. Still further sat a large conference table where breakfast was served.

Although my outer appearance was refreshed from the shower, my head was still half-staff. When I sat down at the table, Benjamin slid a small cup of espresso over to me. Black and strong, it was perfect. Each sip brought me back to life.

We soaked in jazz riffs emanating from the record player as we snacked on blueberry and banana oatmeal paired with sunny-side up eggs, sharing bites of hollow Dutch chocolates we passed around the table as casually as one would a plate of bacon.

After breakfast we hugged our goodbyes, promising to see each other again. I zipped up my backpack and threw on my trashed jacket, war wounds from an awesome night.

Felix and I left for the train station, walking along the Scheveningen Marina in what was left of the sun. The wind continued to wail, but not nearly as powerfully as the night before, leaving the temperature bearable. Arriving at The Hague Centraal Station, we had two different trains to take and his was departing immediately.

"It was really good to see you, Felix! I had so much fun last night. Thanks for the party invite!" I said, sad to see him go.

"You too, Ems! Wish I had more time. I'll see you next time I come over to the States!" We hugged goodbye and he took off down the corridor, jumping onto his train right before the doors slid shut, waving to me through the glass with his goofy grin. My departure was less dramatic and I spent the travel time writing.

Back in Amsterdam, I checked into a private room, packed a bowl of Bubblegum ganja, and walked down to the canal. The streets were dark and quiet away from the center square. It was my secret time in a strange place.

Out alone after midnight soaking up the satisfaction of life, lost in a world of my own making, contemplating everything and nothing at the same time. Those are the moments that create the fuel propelling me forward. Much more goes on in my mind every moment of every day than anyone could dream possible. The minutia of the world never ceases to inspire me.

I was tired as hell when my alarm blared in my ear at 6:00 am. I still had some weed left over when I arrived at Amsterdam Centraal Station so I burned the bright green leaves until they were black and cashed, tossing the pipe into a trash can. Turning around, I smiled farewell to the overcast city, one of my favorites so far.

Commandeering an entire row of seats to myself on the flight home, I buckled up and pulled out my laptop to write. Adventures in Europe left me invigorated and chomping at the bit of life. My wanderlust spirit was given another taste, and, as always, it wanted more.

I renewed my vow to be myself, fully and completely. The best me I could be, squandering no time, squeezing every last drop from each minute, smiling from my heart and never forgetting the beauty of the world and how it was all mine to experience, on my own terms. I was unstoppable.

13 **LIFE IS BEAUTIFUL.**

Ny life came full circle as the weekend of MCA Day 2014 finally arrived. Keeping in touch with the crew over the past year, I had gone from a newbie volunteer to operations manager and event co-host. I was nervous when asked if I would be comfortable on stage with a mic, but responded, "No problem," without hesitation.

Move toward the fear. That was my new motto. When again would I be given the opportunity to host a hip-hop event in Brooklyn, New York honoring not only my favorite musician, but someone who had such a profound impact on my life and perspective? Never. You're not growing if you're not scared.

My backpack carried skinny jeans, an old school three-stripe jacket, 2,000 custom Gratitude stickers, goodie bags, and thank you cards for performers. Boarding my flight, I was psyched for what was to come. I had never hosted an event on-stage in front of strangers, some of whom were hip-hop idols of mine. It was a new challenge

Stepping off of a plane with only a backpack is a freedom hard to describe. The Classon Ave G train subway station felt comfortably familiar, with street signs, pizza places and coffee shops remaining exactly as they were. Dumping my luggage at the loft, I hopped back on the train and I snagged an eighth of Sour Diesel broken into dime sacks from a dude on the stoop of a brownstone on 125th Street. There's a first time for everything.

The event was a blur. I ran around managing the flow of artists to the likes of DJ Hurricane, Cey Adams, Mix Master Mike, and many more, playing Sandman pushing them onstage and yanking those to the wings who surpassed their time limit, emceeing with off-the-cuff humor and freestyled introductions in-between. Meeting hip-hop legends, serving them peanut butter and jelly sandwiches, and being silly with creative people *doing things,* genuine happiness emanated from me.

The energy was vibrating so strongly it splintered my heart into a million pieces that spread out into the universe. I hadn't lost it. I just gave it to the world, continuing my gratitude to the grave. It was a superb weekend punctuated by laughing, hugging, dancing, and ending with a twenty-minute meditation that brought sunshine for weeks.

Awkwardly clutching a gifted five-foot tall canvas painting of MCA, I channeled Jill Clayburgh and lumbered down the bustling streets of Brooklyn. As I twisted and turned through the mass of people on the streets, I caught sight of the world as it only looks from New York City and it suddenly dawned on me.

This is where I belong.

This was where people made things happen out of thin air. I was one of those people. At the intersection of Court and Joralemon early on a sunny Monday, I made the decision to change my life once again. I was moving to Brooklyn.

Trusting my purpose and the universe, I've learned everything tends to work itself out, when you let it. Conquering my dreams day by day, I know that I am anything I want to be. I just have to be it. And so I am.

For I am an American Female, capable of anything, ready for everything. And today, I'm a writer.

THANK YOU

I am grateful you took the time to read
AMERICAN FEMALE.

What did you think of the book? Did you love the adventure?
Who was your favorite character? I want to know it all!

Follow these 3 easy steps:

1. Share a review today on Amazon.com &
   GoodReads.com

2. Instagram, Facebook, or Tweet a selfie with your
   copy of AMERICAN FEMALE

3. Don't forget to tag @american_female and
   hashtag #truetaleofadventure &
   #americanfemalebook

You'll be contacted for shipping information, and a surprise
will arrive at your door. If you post to both Amazon &
GoodReads, you'll get an extra-special gift!

Thanks again - your support means everything.

Always in gratitude.

- Emily

ABOUT THE AUTHOR

EMILY CARPENTER was influenced by writers Olga Levy Drucker and the fabulous James St. James, lyricist Lola "Gangsta Boo" Mitchell, and the legendary Beastie Boys. A recorder of life, hip hop enthusiast, political scientist, and polymath, Emily loves art, music, the ocean, and all the details of the universe. She lives with her strong-willed dog, Bebe, in Saint Louis, Missouri. For more information please visit www.americanfemalebook.com